PREFACE

Since the day the first shiny gold nugget was picked up and coveted, gold has been a powerful lure for the human race. No substance has been more avidly sought throughout history than this rare metal. From Alexander the Great and Julius Caesar to Christopher Columbus, Vasco da Gama, Ferdinand Magellan and Cecil Rhodes, gold has been the driving force for explorers and conquerors alike. The quest for gold even led alchemists to attempt to make it from base metals such as lead and copper.

This book reveals the secrets of where gold is found; tells the exciting story of how people have sought it out from earliest times, through the days of the great gold rushes, to the most modern mines; describes clearly how it is obtained from deep within the ground or from river beds; discusses its unique properties and wide range of uses, from high-technology and dentistry to commerce and ornamentation; and reflects the beauty of this noblest of all metals.

THE AUTHORS

Richard Herrington joined the Department of Mineralogy at The Natural History Museum, London as a researcher in 1991, after working in mineral exploration in industry. Since then, gold has been a major focus of his research, based on linking geological processes with the formation of economic gold deposits.

Chris Stanley is Associate Keeper of Mineralogy at The Natural History Museum, London and a specialist on ore mineralogy, working on the properties, textures and characteristics of mineral deposits. He has more than 20 years' research and consultancy experience.

Robert Symes retired as Keeper of Mineralogy at The Natural History Museum, London in 1997. His still active mineralogical research interests are diverse but he is a particular expert on minerals of the United Kingdom.

CW00404584

Front cover *Hammered and embossed gold pectoral, Calima, Colombia, AD 100-150.*

Facing page *The Golden Fleece, painting by Herbert James Draper, 1904.*

The Natural History Museum is grateful to Rio Tinto plc for supporting the production of this book.

PROPERTIES OF GOLD

The word 'gold' is common throughout the Anglo-Saxon languages and appears to be derived from the Indo-European root *ghel*, meaning 'yellow'. The chemical symbol for the element is Au, from the first two letters of the Latin word *aurum*, which means 'glowing dawn'. Along with mercury, silver and the metals of the platinum group (iridium, osmium, palladium, platinum, rhodium and ruthenium), gold is a noble metal – that is, it resists chemical action, does not tarnish in air or water, and is not easily attacked by acids. Normally, it is soluble only in the very powerful mixture of concentrated hydrochloric and nitric acids known as aqua regia at moderately high temperatures. (When finely divided, however, it may also dissolve in alkaline cyanide solutions.) This general ability to resist chemical attack means that it remains bright. Gold also has the very high melting point of 1063°C.

Together with copper and silver, gold forms the gold group of metals, which have similar properties. All three metals share the same atomic structure built on a face-centred cubic lattice (fig 1). This means that they form crystals with their atoms at the centre of each face as well as at the corners, in the cubic system (with three crystallographic axes of equal length at right angles to one another). They share a similar position in the periodic table of elements, reflecting the similar structure of their atoms, which leads to their similar properties.

ISOTOPES OF GOLD

The atomic number of gold is 79. The atomic number of an element is the number of protons – stable, positively charged elementary particles – found in the nucleus of each of its atoms; this is fixed for a particular element and dictates the element's fundamental physical and chemical properties. The nucleus, however, also contains particles

1 Model showing the face-centred cubic structure of atoms in a gold crystal.

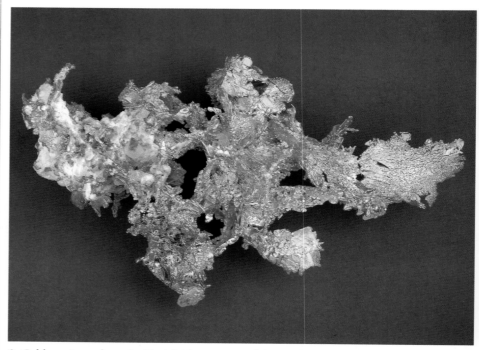

2 Gold specimen from the Eagle's Nest mine, California (length 13 cm).

3 Assortment of gold coins from all over the world.

called neutrons, which add to the atomic weight but can vary in a given element. This gives rise to different isotopes of the element. (Isotopes are forms of the same element whose nuclei contain the same number of protons but different numbers of neutrons.) For example, carbon is found mainly as the isotope carbon-12 (^{12}C), but also occurs as two other natural isotopes ^{13}C and ^{14}C, the numbers referring to their respective atomic weights of 12, 13 and 14. All these isotopes have 6 protons, and thus share the atomic number of 6. There is only one natural isotope of gold, ^{197}Au, but some twenty artificial isotopes can be produced, of which the radioactive isotope ^{198}Au is sometimes used in cancer therapy.

GOLD ALLOYS

In nature, gold occurs mainly mixed, or alloyed, with other metals, there being relatively few known gold compounds (page 7). It is commonly found alloyed with small amounts of silver, with which a full range of solid solutions (solid material in which one substance is uniformly distributed in another) may exist. When pure, the colour of gold is golden-yellow, but when naturally alloyed with silver it becomes paler. When the silver content reaches 20%, the alloy is known as electrum, an ancient name first used by the Roman writer Pliny the Younger about 1900 years ago. Copper, iron and palladium may also be present, but in this case only a limited solid-solution relationship is possible. Like various other metals, gold also readily combines with mercury to form an alloy known as an amalgam.

THE PURITY OF GOLD

The term carat (in the United States, karat) is a measure of the purity of gold, pure gold being 24 carats. Jewellers describe the proportion of gold in an alloy as the number of parts of gold in 24 parts of the alloy, so that 18-carat gold has 6 parts of other metals to make up the total to 24 parts, and 12-carat gold is half gold and half other metals. This use of carat should not be confused with that in the diamond (gemstone) trade, where it is used as a measure of weight. 'Carat' is related to a Greek word meaning a bean from the carob tree of uniform size and weight (fig 4), and also has a link with the Arabic word *kirat*, derived from the Greek, meaning the weight of four grains.

Gold purity is also described in terms of fineness, which is a measure of the gold content in parts per thousand. In this system of measurement, a gold nugget containing 725 parts of pure gold and 275 parts of other metals would be referred to as '725-fine'.

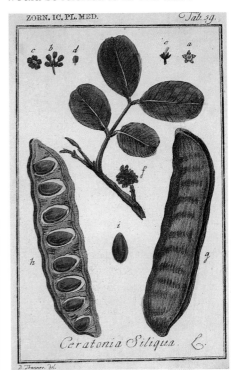

4 Illustration of carob beans used as weights for gems and precious metals.

PHYSICAL PROPERTIES

Gold, gold, gold, gold
Bright and yellow, hard and cold
> **Thomas Hood**, *Her Moral*

Most people see gold only after it has been refined and worked into gold ornaments or jewellery, or perhaps occasionally in bulk as bullion. Its importance in these and other uses is based largely on its physical appearance and its qualities of chemical inertness, high relative density (the ratio of its density to that of water), softness, ductility (the property of a metal enabling it to be drawn out into a wire) and malleability (the property enabling it to be hammered or rolled while cold into different shapes such as flat sheets).

GOLD CRYSTALS

Although its crystals are classified as belonging to the cubic system, gold usually forms octohedral crystals, less often dodecahedral or trapezohedral ones, and only rarely forms cubes (fig 6). Twinned crystals are common, leading to the formation of branching aggregates. These complexities mean that gold crystals are usually irregular and in nature can range from filiform (wire-like), to skeletal (with an open framework structure), reticulated (net-like) or frequently dendritic (branching like a tree, fig 5). Gold crystals do not break neatly to produce smooth surfaces. Instead, when broken, gold shows surfaces with sharp and jagged profiles, in what is known as a 'hackly' fracture.

NUGGETS

Gold may also occur as grains, dust or larger masses, which are referred to as nuggets. The term is usually used to describe the water-worn, rolled masses of gold, often of considerable size, although it can also be used for masses within rocks. The most famous nugget of all – and still the world's largest known example – was the Welcome Stranger nugget from Ballarat, Victoria, Australia (page 39). This nugget may not have travelled far from the rock it formed in. Many nuggets have been transported some distance from where they formed in the rock. They are markedly flattened, and exhibit different degrees of fineness (gold purity), depending on the nature of the gold in the source rock, how far and by what means they travelled (page 13).

6 *The Latrobe gold nugget found at Mt. Ivor, Victoria, Australia, showing its exceptional cubic crystal form (height 10 cm).*

5 *Dendritic gold growth on specimen from Hopes Nose, Devon, England (length 5 cm).*

7 *Diverse gold nuggets from river gravels near Antioqua, Colombia. Deep yellow gold is practically pure whilst the white gold is electrum, an alloy containing significant silver.*

DISTINGUISHING PROPERTIES

Gold has a relative density of 19.3 when pure – much higher than the relative densities of the common alloy metals, copper and silver. The Sicilian Greek mathematician and physicist Archimedes used this property to determine whether a crown was made of pure gold or had been debased by other metals and, in the process, defined his famous principle of buoyancy.

Some of gold's most remarkable properties are its ductility and malleability, since 1 troy ounce (31.1g) can be drawn into a wire more than 100 km long or beaten or pressed as thin as 0.000013 mm, to cover an area of 4 m². Thin gold sheets, known as

8 *Detail of the Fresco of St. Catherine of Alexandria, 1315, decorated with gold leaf.*

gold leaf, can be used to gild artefacts, such as furniture or picture frames (fig 8), and has even been used as a decoration for food.

Gold is used as a contact metal in the electronics industry as it is a good conductor of both electricity and heat (fig 9). In both these respects it is somewhat inferior to copper but because it is inert to chemical breakdown, it is used where reliability is paramount.

Gold is an extremely good reflector of light, not only in the centre of the visible range but also extending well into the infra-red part of the spectrum. This ability to reflect infra-red wavelengths makes it a very useful material for shielding the sensitive parts of spacecraft and missiles against radiant heat, as well as serving as a thermal insulator in some modern window glasses.

Gold is very soft, with a hardness of between 2 and 3 on the Mohs' scale, in which talc (the mineral hydrated magnesium silicate, from which talcum powder is ground) is 1 and diamond is 10. To increase the hardness for everyday use and also to vary its colour when used in jewellery, gold is often alloyed with other metals. Nickel, platinum, silver or zinc may be added to give a pale or white gold, copper for red and for a tinge of blue, iron. Other metals of the platinum group, such as iridium, rhodium and palladium, have also been used to harden gold. These alloys are often found naturally (fig 7).

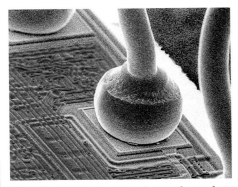

9 *Gold microwires bonded to a silicon chip on a computer circuit board.*

MINERALOGY OF GOLD

'Gold is the child of Zeus, neither moth nor rust devoureth it but the mind of man is devoured'

[Pindar, 5th century BC**]**

Gold is stable in the metallic form over a wide range of conditions. It prefers its 'native' state and it is therefore found mostly in the form of native gold or as gold alloys with copper or silver.

In rocks and veins, or lodes (pages 14-21), gold is most commonly associated with silver as a gold-silver alloy (fig 10). It can also form natural alloys with antimony (fig 11), bismuth, lead, mercury, palladium and platinum. Gold may form compounds with selenium, sulphur or tellurium. Indeed, some telluride minerals of gold, such as calaverite, krennerite, petzite, and sylvanite, are relatively common in certain deposits (notably at Kalgoorlie, Australia; Sacarimb, Romania; Cripple Creek and Bisbee, USA (fig 12)), whereas gold tellurium sulphides, such as buckhornite (fig 14) and nagyagite, as well as gold selenide (fig 13) and sulphide minerals, are extremely rare. Gold also forms oxides in association with antimony, tellurium and tin, although these are very poorly studied. Gold can be present as sub-microscopic particles in some sulphide minerals, such as pyrite (FeS_2) and arsenopyrite (FeAsS), in which form it is particularly difficult to extract, and is referred to as 'invisible', or refractory gold.

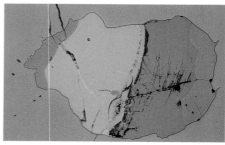

12 Reflected light photomicrograph of a telluride-native metal-sulphide assemblage from the Campbell Orebody, Bisbee, Arizona, USA. Bright yellow gold occurs close to white lead telluride (altaite), and cuts the creamy gold telluride (calaverite). The other minerals are grey lead sulphide (galena), pale yellow iron sulphide (pyrite) and slightly greenish-yellow copper iron sulphide (chalcopyrite). (Horizontal field about 0.3 mm).

10 Reflected light photomicrograph showing grains of bright yellow native gold and creamy gold-silver alloy (electrum), together with the minerals grey lead sulphide (galena), and pale yellow iron sulphide (pyrite). Specimen from the Tukilinsky gold prospect, Kazakhstan. (Horizontal field about 0.3 mm).

11 Reflected light digital image of the white gold-antimony alloy called aurostibite, together with the complex, rare, grey mineral thallium silver gold antimony sulphide, known as criddleite. Specimen from the Golden Giant mine, Hemlo, Ontario, Canada. (Horizontal field about 0.3 mm)

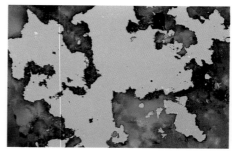

13 Reflected light photomicrograph revealing grey areas of the silver gold selenide mineral fischesserite, together with bright white grains of native gold, in a greenish matrix of copper selenates and copper carbonates. Specimen from Hopes Nose, Devon, England. (Horizontal field about 0.3 mm)

In placer deposits gold is largely present in native form or as the alloy electrum. As gold becomes liberated from the host rock by weathering, gold compounds are broken down and only native gold and alloys remain. There is some evidence that silver may be lost from the electrum during weathering to leave a more gold rich alloy. Some of the nuggets of gold found in placer deposits have gold rich rinds to them where silver has been dissolved away during contact with groundwater.

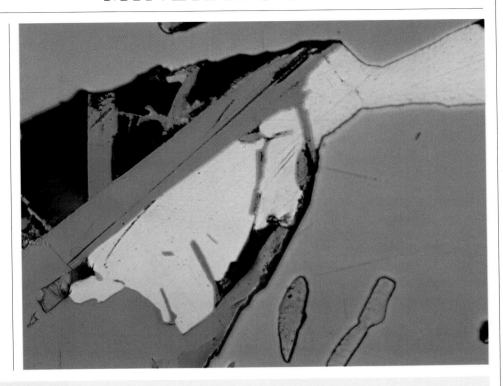

14 Reflected light photomicrograph showing bright yellow native gold associated with thin grey bands of the rare mineral gold lead bismuth sulphotelluride (buckhornite), occupying cavities within pale yellow iron sulphide (pyrite). Specimen from the Buckhorn Mine, Boulder County, Colorado, USA. (Horizontal field about 0.5 mm.)

TABLE 1. THE MINERAL DIVERSITY OF GOLD

Mineral	Formula	Mineral	Formula	Mineral	Formula
NATIVE GOLD AND ALLOYS		TELLURIDES		SELENIDES AND SULPHIDES	
gold	Au	calaverite	$AuTe_2$	uytenbogaardtite	Ag_3AuS_2
electrum	$(Au_{0.5-0.8},Ag_{0.2-0.5})$	krennerite	$(Au,Ag)Te_2$	nagyagite	$Pb_{13}Au_2Sb_3Te_6S_{16}$
aurostibite	$AuSb_2$	petzite	Ag_3AuTe_2	buckhornite	$AuPb_2BiTe_2S_3$
auricupride	Cu_3Au	sylvanite	$AgAuTe_4$	criddleite	$TlAg_2Au_3Sb_{10}S_{10}$
tetraauricupride	$CuAu$	kostovite	$CuAuTe_4$	penzhinite	$Ag_4Au(S,Se)_4$
hunchunite	Au_2Pb	montbrayite	Au_2Te_3	petrovskaite	$AuAg(S,Se)$
maldonite	Au_2Bi	bogdanovite	$Au_5(Cu,Fe)_3(Te,Pb)_2$	fischesserite	Ag_3AuSe_2
weishanite	$(Au,Ag)_3Hg_2$	bezsmertnovite	$(Au,Ag)_4Cu(Te,Pb)$		
anyuiite	$AuPb_2$	bilibinskite	$Au_3Cu_2PbTe_2$		
yuanjiangite	$AuSn$	muthmannite	$(Au,Ag)Te$		
zvyagintsevite	$(Pd,Pt,Au)_3(Pb,Sn)$				

WHERE GOLD IS FOUND

Gold is a rare metal – on average, our planet contains less than a third of a gram per tonne of its rock. This includes the earth's metallic core, which is enriched in gold by up to five times this amount. Excluding the enriched core, the thin strip of crust making up the continents we live on contains an average of only 5 mg of gold for each tonne of rock. At this concentration, we would need to take all the gold from at least 2000 tonnes of average crust to make even the most modest wedding ring. This tiny proportion is generally present as isolated atoms of gold distributed as impurities in the minerals that make up the rock. However, in a few localities gold is found in concentrated amounts and can be extracted by mining.

Gold is also present in the oceans, in minute concentrations that average about 0.02 mg (20μg) of gold per litre of seawater. Since the oceans consist of more than 1×10^{21} litres of seawater, they contain a total of over 20 million tonnes of gold. However, even with the 1999 gold price of about US$300 dollars per troy oz (31.1 g) – which potentially makes the sea worth a staggering US$200,000,000,000,000 in gold value – the cost of extraction is too great to be contemplated at the moment.

In the context of mining, the term 'ore' is used for a mineral or combination of minerals from which a useful substance, for example a metal such as gold, can be extracted and

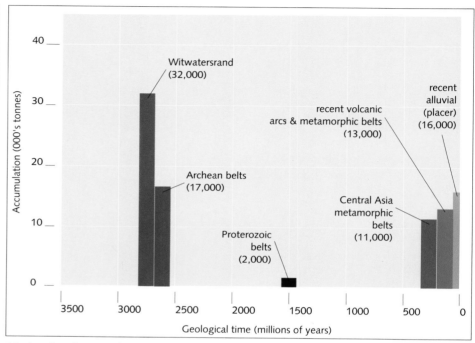

15 *Age distribution of gold deposits through geological time.*

marketed at a profit. Modern gold mines exploit ores for which the gold values average between 2 and 10 g of gold per tonne of rock – up to 2000 times the average concentration in the earth's crust. Even at this level of economic extraction, gold is still unlikely to be visible to the naked eye in the ore. Usually, the gold content of a rock must reach about 30 g per tonne before gold is clearly visible even under a hand lens.

Gold ore deposits are found in rocks formed throughout the earth's history, dating from the early Precambrian era,

TABLE 2. AVERAGE VALUES FOR GOLD ON THE EARTH (in g/tonne)

Seawater:	0.000012
Continental crust:	0.003–0.005
Oceanic crust:	0.005–0.007
Conglomerates:	0.03
Coal measures:	up to 2.1
Earth's core:	0.4–2.5
Typical gold ore:	1.0–10.0

more than 3 billion years ago, to the present. However, the most significant gold deposits are related to distinct

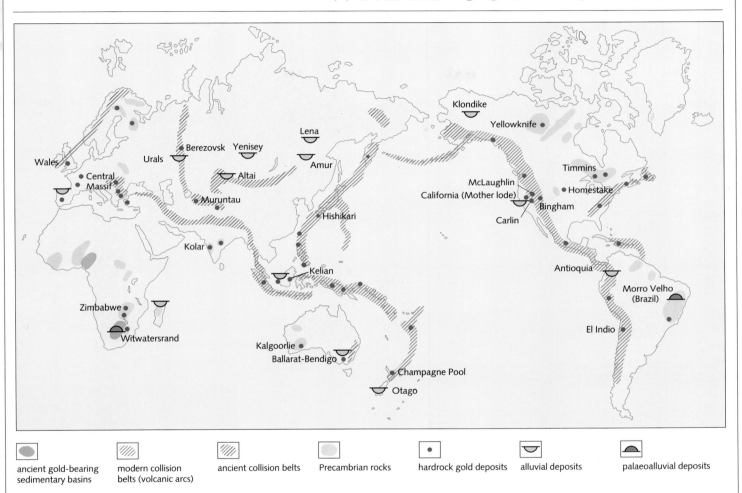

16 *World map showing major gold deposits.*

Legend:
- ancient gold-bearing sedimentary basins
- modern collision belts (volcanic arcs)
- ancient collision belts
- Precambrian rocks
- hardrock gold deposits
- alluvial deposits
- palaeoalluvial deposits

periods in the earth's history (fig 15), and ancient and modern collision belts (fig 16). Recent alluvial deposits have been the primary source of much of the ancient gold and they continue to be an important source. The ancient deposits in the Archean belts and the Witwatersrand basin of South Africa dominate as sources of the world's gold. Modern volcanic arcs, particularly those around the Pacific ocean, together with older geologically equivalent rocks, are an increasingly important target for modern gold miners.

Geologists know that gold deposits are forming today in some active geothermal areas. Studying the geological processes occuring in these areas provides them with the clues they need to show how gold deposits may have formed in ancient rocks.

HOW GOLD ACCUMULATES

Gold deposits form at the earth's surface today by two distinctively different mechanisms. Because of the resistance of gold to weathering, it survives the process of rock erosion at the surface and can become mechanically concentrated into 'placer', or alluvial, deposits – those transported downstream by rivers. The other way in which gold becomes concentrated is by hydrothermal activity, whereby gold dissolves in certain fluids, which transport it until it precipitates from solution.

WHEN GOLD DISSOLVES

The fluids that are able to do this must contain other components (ions or ligands) that are able to help gold dissolve. Surface waters, such as rivers, are normally poor at dissolving gold, since they are cool and generally contain few ions capable of dissolving and transporting gold. In some tropical soils, however, the groundwater may carry acids derived from rotting vegetation (organic acids) that have been shown to dissolve gold. In some areas, traces of natural cyanide have also been found that will dissolve gold extremely well. This valuable property of cyanide is now employed in many gold mines, where cyanide compounds are used in the extraction of gold from its ore.

HYDROTHERMAL FLUIDS

Gold can also be dissolved by the heated waters that circulate in deeper parts of the earth's crust. These are known collectively as hydrothermal fluids (the word 'hydrothermal' coming from the Greek words for 'hot water'). They often contain either significant amounts of dissolved halogen ions, such as chloride and bromide, or sulphur-bearing complexes, which can also dissolve and transport gold.

In some deposits, gold is found together with tellurium and selenium, and ions of these elements may also transport gold in solution. In some rare cases gold may even be carried as sub-microscopic particles in the form of a colloid (fig 17). The presence of gold colloids has been used by some researchers to explain how really high-grade gold grades, referred to by miners as 'bonanza gold', may occur in some veins (fig 18).

Since geologists know that the amount of gold in an average crustal rock must be enriched about 2000 times to make an economic gold deposit, large volumes of fluid must be circulated through the crust by geological processes to form gold ores. This is because even where the gold contents can be measured in hydrothermal fluids saturated with gold (that is, fluids that have dissolved as much of the metal as they can), as little as 0.014 parts per million may be present.

However, in areas of the earth's crust where there is hydrothermal fluid activity today – such as hot-springs and earthquake zones – enough fluid is circulating through them to produce

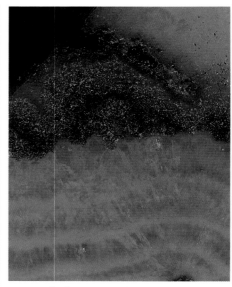

17 Finely disseminated gold in the white-banded silica mineral chalcedony. Specimen from Koch Bulak gold mine, Uzbekistan (width of image 2 mm).

18 Spectacular, high-grade bonanza gold with a 'platy' appearance (occurring in thin, leaflike layers) from the Sacarimb (formerly known as Nagyag) gold deposit, Romania (height of sample 5 cm).

gold deposits of the size that are now mined commercially. Geologists can look for evidence of these processes in ancient rocks as a guide to where new gold deposits might be found.

HYDROTHERMAL DEPOSITS

The term 'hydrothermal', sometimes used synonymously with geothermal, encompasses all types of hot-water phenomena that occur in the earth's crust. Places where hydrothermal activity occurs in the crust can be broadly subdivided into continental areas, where the crust is hotter than normal, and areas linked to active plate tectonic processes, such as volcanic arcs or spreading ridges. Hydrothermal activity is evident in the form of the geysers, hot springs and mud-pools visible on the earth's surface. Examples of this hydrothermal activity can be seen in Yellowstone National Park, USA, in parts of Iceland and in the Taupo volcanic zone of New Zealand. In some of these active areas, geologists have found gold deposits forming.

The ability of hydrothermal systems to move dissolved metals around relates to the types of water circulated, the chemistry of the waters and the way the waters evolve in the system – whether they boil, cool or mix with other fluids. Many hydrothermal systems are associated with metal ores, but only those with the right water chemistry and suitable source rocks from which to derive the gold are associated with the metal.

SEAFLOOR SMOKERS AND HOT SPRING DEPOSITS

On the seafloor, active tectonic zones where new crust is forming (spreading centres) are associated with hot springs, called hydrothermal vents. These are known as black or white smokers because the superheated water that issues from them contains finely divided mineral grains, forming what appears to be smoke. In the Pacific, such springs are responsible for depositing significant amounts of gold on the seafloor (fig 19). Similarly, terrestrial hot springs in active volcanic arcs, such as those in North Island, New Zealand, and in California, are precipitating quantities of gold.

Further evidence that gold can be concentrated in hot-spring systems has been found when the scale collecting on the pipes in a New Zealand geothermal power station was examined. In addition to silica, metal sulphides, sulphates and other minerals, the deposits were found to contain large amounts of gold. In the Champagne Pool at Waiotapu, close to the geothermal power station with its gold-rich pipe-scale, hydrothermal water flows at 10 litres per second, carrying dissolved gold (fig 20). Calculations show that this system is likely to be precipitating about 4 kg of gold per year in and around the pool. At this rate, a potentially economic gold deposit might form at Waiotapu in as little as 50,000 years, which is negligible in geological terms.

19 Black smoker vent in the East Pacific Rise, at great depth on the Pacific Ocean floor, precipitating metallic minerals, including gold.

20 Champagne pool, Waiotapu, New Zealand.

HOW GOLD ACCUMULATES

PLACER GOLD DEPOSITS

Placer, or alluvial, deposits of gold result from the erosion and washing away of gold contained in rocks by the action of wind or flowing water. Gold is highly resistant to chemical attack in streams and its malleability and high relative density mean that it becomes concentrated in the most active parts of river systems.

In antiquity, the bulk of gold production came from the working of river gravels, both active and ancient, since the extraction technology is very simple and discovery of the gold ores is relatively straightforward. The earliest known gold extraction came from washing river gravels and many ancient myths (such as the famous story of Jason and the Golden Fleece) relate to the washing of gold in river courses.

As they exist today, placers relate either to present drainage systems or to former channels where erosion and redeposition has ceased. Gold placers generally relate to mountain belts where there has been a significant uplift of gold-bearing rocks. This is because the process of forming mountains is linked to tectonic activity, which may have formed the gold deposits in the rock, and because uplift has resulted in deep erosion of the rocks releasing the gold. Placer gold forms after the major mountain-building tectonic activity has ceased, when the erosion of the uplifted areas is linked to widespread deposition in large river systems. This can be seen in North America, where erosion of the Rocky Mountains has led to the formation of the placer deposits in north-west Canada and Alaska.

Although placers can be broadly traced to likely regions of bedrock source gold, in many cases the fabled 'mother lode' sought by miners has often eluded explorers upstream from large placer deposits, perhaps because these source areas have now been highly eroded.

TYPES OF PLACER DEPOSITS

The main types of placer deposits are known as eluvial, colluvial and fluvial. Eluvial deposits are those where gold becomes concentrated as more soluble components are removed, a process that occurs particularly in warm climates. The Romans were aware of these types of deposits and exploited enriched layers of gold-bearing muds, formed as low-grade sulphide ores became weathered in Cyprus and at Rio Tinto, Spain. This process of weathering can significantly improve the grade of an original ore and also breaks down the ore, often making the gold available to be extracted by cheaper technologies.

Colluvial placers form downslope from a bedrock gold deposit where the rock waste is gradually moving downwards, after being eroded and weathered.

Fluvial placers form in flowing water downstream from the bedrock source region in active river channels. These placers may travel long distances downstream but most form only about 15 km from the bedrock source. Bars and islands of braided streams, where the deposits of gravel accumulate, are particularly good places for gold to become concentrated. The gravel deposits generally grow in the direction of river flow, with the upstream ends of river bars becoming enriched in gold (fig 30).

These deposits have been extensively mined since prehistoric times. The Romans developed alluvial gold mining to a high degree, processing vast river gravel deposits such as Las Medulas in Spain (fig 71) and the Po basin gravels

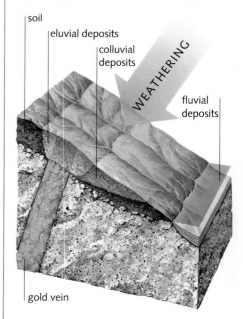

21 *Diagram showing how eluvial, colluvial and fluvial deposits are formed.*

of northern Italy. Centuries later, the great gold rushes also focused on alluvial gold areas such as California, the Yukon river of Canada and Alaska and South Island, New Zealand.

Depending on the source areas, gold accumulates with other dense and resistant minerals, including diamond, cassiterite, iron-zirconium-titanium oxides (collectively known as 'black sands') and platinum (figs 22 and 23). Alluvial gold often contains larger nuggets, and the gold is of greater fineness than the bedrock gold. This leads some researchers to believe that gold may accrete due to its malleable nature, and that elements such as silver that are contained in the bedrock gold may be leached from it during weathering. Some gold may also have formed by authigenic, or *in-situ*, growth of nuggets.

23 *Diamond embedded in a gold nugget found in Brazilian alluvial gravels.*

24 *Women panning for gold, Central Mindanao, Philippines.*

22 *Gold with 'black sands' in a gold pan.*

GOLD IN METAMORPHIC ROCKS

Gold-bearing quartz veins, or lodes, are common in many ancient mountain belts around the world. These veins are faults, or fractures in rocks, that have become infilled with minerals precipitated from hydrothermal fluids. Gold may form coarse aggregates, associated with quartz, minor sulphide minerals, such as pyrite, and often carbonate minerals.

MESOTHERMAL DEPOSITS

These vein deposits are commonly referred to as mesothermal gold deposits; the term mesothermal means 'medium heat', referring to the temperatures (about 250–350°C) under which the deposits formed in the earth. Mesothermal deposits are common in the very oldest known, Archaean-age, volcanic belts (more than 2.5 billion years old), which are known as greenstone belts. Classic areas for such gold deposits are the ancient 'shield' areas of Canada (at Yellowknife and Timmins), Australia (Kalgoorlie), Zimbabwe and Brazil.

These ancient deposits appeared to have formed at the time that many geologists believe there was a worldwide gold 'event' some 2.6 billion years ago, linked perhaps to the start of plate tectonics as we know it today. However, mesothermal deposits are also found in younger mountain belts, such as the Palaeozoic slate belts of South Australia (at Ballarat-Bendigo), Nova Scotia and Europe (for example, those in Wales and the Massif Central of France) as well as Mesozoic belts, such as the Californian Mother Lode.

Typically, both these deposit types are represented by classic vein systems (lodes) that cut through the usually highly metamorphosed host rocks. Distinctive ribbon veins form as the vein repeatedly opens and becomes filled by white quartz, sulphides and gold (fig 25). Studies of minute trapped drops of fluids in the quartz crystals show that the fluids contained not only

25 *Typical ribboned quartz-sulphide-gold veins from the Patchway gold mine, Zimbabwe.*

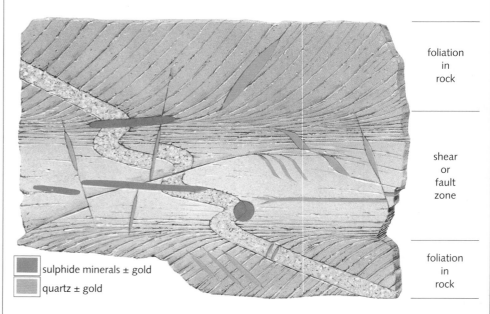

foliation in rock

shear or fault zone

foliation in rock

sulphide minerals ± gold

quartz ± gold

26 *Schematic diagram showing the diverse styles of gold deposits in large fault or shear zones.*

dissolved salts (at a concentration of about 2–5% by weight of salts), but also dissolved carbon dioxide gas.

GOLD VEIN FORMATION

Further research has shown that at the time of each event that formed the individual ribbon of gold-bearing vein, the carbon dioxide was actually unmixing from the fluid. This is directly comparable to the way that opening a can of lemonade or beer causes carbon dioxide to fizz and escape from the drink. In the case of the gold vein, it was the opening of the fault that caused this loss of carbon dioxide from the fluid, which can be linked to the chemical

changes that cause both the gold and other vein minerals to form.

This unmixing of the fluid probably relates to the fault fracturing during earthquake activity, allowing the pressurized fluid to blow its top and precipitate minerals in the fault zone. Other deposits show the gold more disseminated in altered zones around fault systems but they share features of formation with large quartz vein deposits – namely, the importance of large-scale fault systems (shear zones , and evidence of large volumes of fluids having flowed through these zones (fig 26 . Gold and other minerals such as quartz infill the cracks formed during faulting.

NEW ASIAN GOLDFIELDS

The large vein deposits of gold in rocks of Palaeozoic age in Central Asia are possibly of this type. The largest of these is that found at Muruntau in the Kyzyl Kum desert west of the Tien Shan mountains in Uzbekistan (fig 28). This has ore reserves of some 4500 tonnes of gold, making it one of the most significant goldfields in the world outside South Africa. The Muruntau deposits show many similarities to those found within metamorphic rocks in Archaean and mountain belts of various ages (fig 27), but may in fact be linked to large granitic intrusive magma bodies which occur nearby or at depth.

27 Gold-bearing quartz veins in metamorphic host rocks, Muruntau, Uzbekistan.

28 View over the enormous Muruntau open pit gold mine, Uzbekistan.

GOLD IN ANCIENT SEDIMENTS

RAND-STYLE GOLD DEPOSITS

Since their discovery, the mines in the Witwatersrand basin of South Africa (usually known simply as 'the Rand'), have provided over half of all the world's mined gold. Gold was first discovered in the Rand at the end of the 19th century. While there is some debate as to the exact date and the identity of the first find, the discovery of the rich 'Main Reef' was made in March 1886 and this led to the gold mining boom (page 40). Over a hundred years later, the Rand still produces more than 470 tonnes of gold every year, with a value of some US$7 billion.

Even so, just how long this production will continue from the ever-deeper mining operations is unclear. Some of the mines currently work up to 4 km below the surface. This is deep enough in the earth for rock temperatures to reach 40°C, so that the mine must be refrigerated. Also, the rocks are under such pressure from the load above that the exposed faces would shatter spontaneously if the walls were not strongly protected.

CONGLOMERATE BEDS

The Rand gold occurs in Archaean-age pebbly sediments (conglomerates) dated at between 3.1 and 2.75 billion years old (fig 29). These conglomerates are part of a gold-bearing sequence of sedimentary and volcanic rocks more than 11 km thick in a basin covering an area of some 270 km by 100 km. The presence of the pebbly conglomerates gives a clue that they formed as part of ancient braided river channels. The gold found in the conglomerate channels occurs in zones formerly known to Boer miners as 'banket', after a popular type of lumpy almond toffee, but now more commonly called 'reef'. Electrum containing both mercury and zinc, as well as silver, is found together with other minerals, such as pyrite, between the pebbles in the conglomerate. Many uranium-bearing minerals are also associated with the gold.

The Rand conglomerate beds have been compared to modern gold-bearing placer deposits in rivers (fig 30). The traditional interpretation of how these deposits formed suggests that they are ancient gold-bearing river gravels (or 'palaeo-placers'). The host rocks are undoubtedly conglomerates of some type that are likely to have formed in braided river channels, but there are many problems with such a simple mechanical gold-concentration model.

Recent research shows that much or all of the gold crystallized well after the deposition of the conglomerate beds. There is also other evidence for the large-scale movement of hydrothermal fluids through the Witwatersrand

29 *'Banket' conglomerate gold ore from the Witwatersrand region of South Africa. The shiny, brassy mineral between the white and grey quartz pebbles is pyrite (iron sulphide, or 'fools gold'). The real gold is invisible in the matrix of pebbles.*

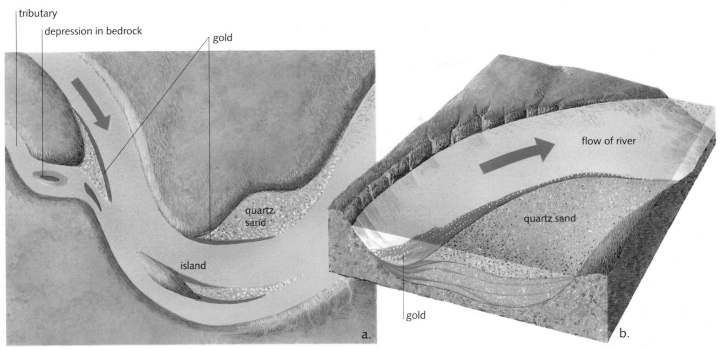

tributary

depression in bedrock

gold

gold

quartz sand

island

flow of river

quartz sand

gold

a.

b.

30 a) Plan view of where gold accumulates in active river systems.
b) Gold is most highly enriched at the edge of the most active parts of the river.

conglomerates after they were deposited, supporting the idea that much of the gold was introduced by these later hot solutions. However, none of the geological models can explain the ultimate source of such a vast amount of gold (45,000 tonnes).

Other gold deposits comparable to those of the Rand are found in Precambrian rocks of Canada, Brazil and Ghana. Since in all cases, the gold occurs in pebbly conglomerates formed as ancient river gravels, an alluvial origin is the most simple explanation.

IRON FORMATION DEPOSITS

In some Precambrian areas, iron-rich sedimentary rocks known as 'banded iron formations' (BIFs) contain economic gold deposits. Here, the rocks are highly metamorphosed and faulted, and show alteration caused by later hydrothermal fluids. This has led many geologists to propose that they formed in the same way as other metamorphic gold deposits, with the gold becoming introduced into the rocks after metamorphism. The iron-rich rocks are brittle and

would break up during faulting to leave open spaces through which hydrothermal fluid could flow. Hydrothermal fluid moving through the rock could react with the iron-rich minerals of the BIF, precipitating out the gold and forming iron-bearing sulphide minerals.

However, some sulphide-rich ores like those at Bousquet in Quebec, Canada, may have their origin in processes similar to those at modern seafloor vent sites, and might be similar to VHMS deposits (page 20).

GOLD IN SEDIMENTARY ROCKS

CARLIN-TYPE DEPOSITS

Another major class of gold deposit is the Carlin-type deposit. The name refers to the best example of the deposit, which was found at Carlin, Nevada, USA. It includes gold deposits in sediments, which are generally found in carbonate-rich rocks but which may also relate to the presence of nearby intrusive rocks (magma bodies that have intruded into pre-existing rocks). Carlin-type deposits are also found in sedimentary rocks in Barney's Canyon, in Utah, USA, in parts of southern China and in the Bau region of Malaysia. For the deposits in Malaysia and Utah, the link with the same kind of magmatic bodies that contain porphyry copper deposits is clear, whereas in the case of the deposits at Carlin itself, the link with such rocks is considered by many geologists as speculative.

In Nevada, Carlin-type deposits are found in Palaeozoic-age carbonate rocks and occur in distinctive 'trends' (linear distributions relating to a geological feature). This supports the idea of a deep-fault system that controls where the deposits formed. The deposits lie close to a large, near-horizontal fault zone, which may be significant because fluids can travel along or be trapped within such zones.

Another striking feature of Carlin-type deposits is that the mineralized gold occurs in specific sites, in a similar geological setting to that of an oilfield

31 Aerial view of part of the Carlin Trend in Nevada, USA, showing the alignment of the open pit gold mines.

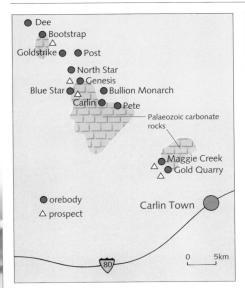

32 Schematic map of the Carlin Trend.

where oil is found trapped in rocks. In many cases, the gold ore occurs with, or close to, hydrocarbon-bearing rocks. This suggests one of two possibilities. Either the movement of hot, gold-bearing solutions may be linked with oil migration or the presence of hydrocarbons may help precipitate the gold from solution. Also, the rocks surrounding the gold deposits often show dramatic evidence of alteration by the corrosive hydrothermal fluids.

The Carlin type of deposit was first recognized by US geologists in 1960, and from 1965 to 1998 the Carlin group of mines has produced more than 700 tonnes of gold. Current production from this area stands at 47 tonnes of gold per year. Associated with gold in the Carlin

33 Hydrocarbon-rich rocks, associated with gold ore, at the Carlin gold deposit.

deposits are barium, antimony and arsenic. The main mineral associated with gold at Carlin is pyrite (FeS_2), which is found along with barite ($BaSO_4$), orpiment (As_2S_3), realgar (AsS) and stibnite (Sb_2S_3). There are also high levels of silver, mercury and thallium within the deposits.

GOLD ASSOCIATED WITH VOLCANOES

Many gold deposits are related to modern and ancient plate tectonic boundaries where either new crust is forming (spreading centres) or being destroyed (subduction zones).

VHMS DEPOSITS

In areas where new crust formed in the distant past, geologists have found evidence of fissures in the ocean floor similar to today's hot-spring black and white 'smoker' systems (page 11). They are preserved in mountain belts where fragments of former oceans have been uplifted and eroded by plate tectonic processes. These ancient seafloor hot-springs often form ore deposits, which are currently mined for their metal contents, including, in many cases, significant amounts of gold (figs 34 and 35).

34 Photograph showing the open pit mine of Yaman Kasy in the Ural Mountains of Russia. The floor of the open pit consists of gold-bearing grey sulphide ore, which formed at a black smoker vent over 400 million years ago.

This type of deposit is generally referred to as 'volcanic-hosted massive sulphide', or VHMS. Some VHMS deposits occur in rocks more than 2.7 billion years old, while others have been found in rocks through geological time up to the present day. Their existence through geological time gives geologists some of the clearest evidence that black and white smoker hot-spring activity probably started on the earth just as soon as the planet formed oceans.

EPITHERMAL DEPOSITS

At the beginning of the 20th century, the great American ore geologist Waldemar Lindgren, among others, recognized that many ancient gold deposits had features comparable to present-day zones of active geothermal activity in continental areas. He linked preserved features, such as layered, silica-containing, hot-spring deposits (sinters), that can also be seen today at

35 Fossils of worm tubes preserved in ancient vents, found in sulphide ore at the Yaman Kasy mine, Urals, Russia. The tubes are believed to have been made by ancestors of the same types of tube worms seen at black smoker vent sites today.

active geothermal sites like Yellowstone, northwest USA, to similar rocks preserved in many gold deposits, such as those of the Comstock Lode in Nevada. Lindgren coined the term 'epithermal' to describe these gold deposits. Derived from the Greek, this word simply means 'low temperature'.

STRATOVOLCANOES

In areas where oceanic plates collide with other oceanic or continental plates, the denser oceanic crust undergoes a process known as subduction, as it is forced beneath more buoyant continental crust or other oceanic crust.

Subduction zones are marked by earthquakes and chains of volcanoes known as 'volcanic arcs'. In these areas the melting of crust from the plate forced under results in the volcanic activity at the surface. Ocean floor rocks are 'wet' and the melting of this crust forms volatile water and gas-rich magma. This gives rise to 'stratovolcanoes', which are formed of interlayered lava and ash. The very destructive volcanism seen at Mt St Helens in the western USA, Mt Pinotubo in the Philippines, and the Soufrière Hills of Montserrat in the Caribbean are all examples of this type of explosive, gassy volcanism.

Because of their abundant volatiles, which can leach and transport dissolved metals, such volcanoes and related deeper magmatic bodies are important sites for mineralization.

36 *The dramatic eruption of Mt St Helens, a volcanic peak in the Cascade range, Washington, USA, in May 1980.*

37 *Famous example of a porphyry copper deposit: the Bingham Canyon copper-gold mine in Utah, USA, which is the largest artificial excavation on our planet.*

HIGH-SULPHIDATION DEPOSITS

In the upper volcanic parts of these arcs, volatiles from the magma, rich in sulphur, interact with groundwaters, producing sulphuric acid that literally digests the volcanic rocks through which it passes. In these distinctive, acid-leached, white rocks, low-temperature (epithermal) gold-copper ore deposits form, which are termed 'high-sulphidation' ores, because much of the sulphur is present in the oxidized sulphate form. Typical high-sulphidation deposits are found at Chinkuashih in Taiwan, where sulphur-rich fumaroles are testament to volatiles continuing to escape from magmas at depth.

LOW-SULPHIDATION DEPOSITS

Farther from the actual volcano itself – or else later as its activity wanes – remnant heat from the volcanic process results in surface hot-spring activity, which is also related to gold mineralization. Compared to the high-sulphidation fluids, these are much less acid and the sulphur present is in the reduced sulphide form. These 'low-sulphidation' gold deposits are directly comparable to hot-spring areas, such as Champagne Pool in New Zealand (page 11).

A good example of a low-sulphidation deposit is the Hishikari deposit in Japan, where hot water still flows from the rocks underground. The McLaughlin mine (fig 70) in California and Comstock Lode in Nevada are similar.

DEEPER GOLD DEPOSITS

Deeper down in some of these volcanic systems, the magma bodies which fed the overlying volcanoes are mineralized with copper and gold. Water-rich fluids separating from the liquid magma as it cooled formed the important group of deposits known as porphyry copper deposits. These have molybdenum and gold associated with them. In favourably eroded areas, these low-grade, but large deposits have been exposed and are currently mined, mainly for their copper and molybdenum, but also for gold.

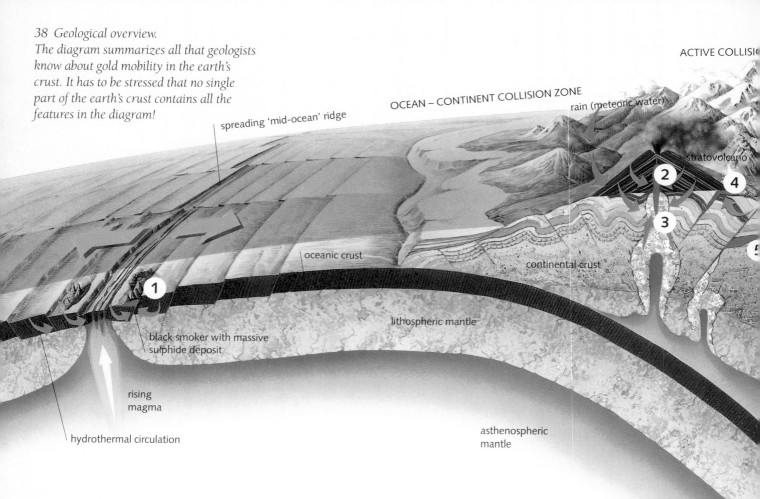

38 *Geological overview.*
The diagram summarizes all that geologists know about gold mobility in the earth's crust. It has to be stressed that no single part of the earth's crust contains all the features in the diagram!

ACTIVE COLLISI

OCEAN – CONTINENT COLLISION ZONE

spreading 'mid-ocean' ridge

rain (meteoric water)

stratovolcano

oceanic crust

continental crust

black smoker with massive sulphide deposit

lithospheric mantle

rising magma

asthenospheric mantle

hydrothermal circulation

1) Black smoker and massive sulphide deposit. Circulating seawater is heated leaching metals which form mineral deposits including gold on the seafloor (page 11).

Stratovolcano
2) In the upper parts of these systems, 'high sulphidation' epithermal gold deposits may form from condensed magmatic gases and circulating rain water (page 20).

3) Below, within or close to the feeder magma chamber, magmatic fluids may produce porphyry copper deposits which contain significant gold (page 20).

4) Hot spring and 'low sulphidation' epithermal gold deposit.
Heated groundwaters carry dissolved gold from deeper igneous rocks to form shallow gold deposits in volcanic arcs (page 21).

5) Carlin-type gold deposits.
Gold deposits form in carbonate rocks close to major fault systems which may carry gold-bearing fluids from deep magma bodies.

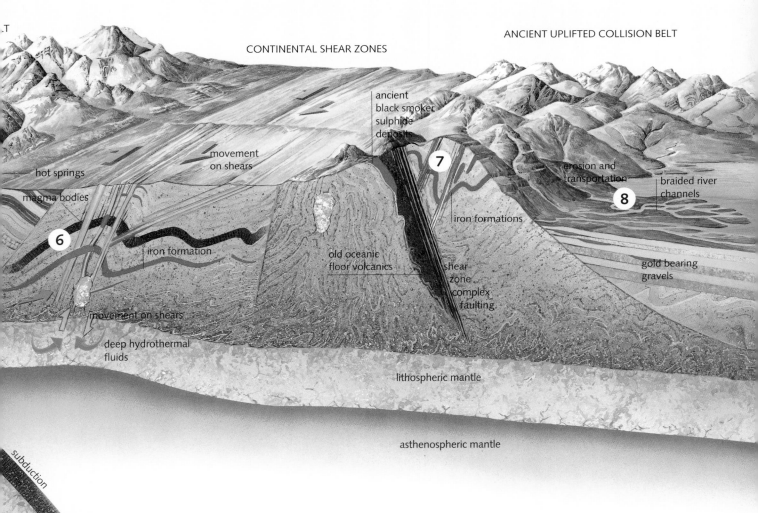

CONTINENTAL SHEAR ZONES

ANCIENT UPLIFTED COLLISION BELT

.T

ancient
black smoker
sulphide
deposits

movement
on shears

7

erosion and
transportation

braided river
channels

hot springs

8

magma bodies

iron formations

6

iron formation

old oceanic
floor volcanics

shear
zone
complex
faulting

gold bearing
gravels

movement on shears

deep hydrothermal
fluids

lithospheric mantle

asthenospheric mantle

subduction

6) Gold in metamorphic rocks.
Large continent-scale faults focus the intrusion of
magma bodies and the circulation of gold-
bearing fluids during tectonic activity. Gold is
moved through these structures to become
deposited in favourable sites such as iron-
formations, quartz veins or disseminated zones
(pages 14 and 15).

7) Ancient collision belt.
Ancient examples of the types of deposits
formed in modern oceans and collision belts may
be found in ancient belts, evidence of similar
gold deposit-forming processes active
throughout the geological record.

8) Gold in sedimentary basins.
Gold deposits are eroded but not dissolved as a
result of physical processes at the earth's surface.
As a result, gold grains or nuggets are carried by
moving water (or wind) to be redeposited in
favourable sites in rivers and lakes. These
accumulations become preserved as the
sediments are changed to rocks. Such processes
explain modern alluvial deposits (page 17) and
perhaps the large ancient deposits of the
Witwatersrand (page 16).

EXPLORATION

The first account of gold mining was written by the Greek geographer and historian Strabo (c. 64 BC to c. AD 23). In his great 17-volume work *Geographia*, he wrote what was probably the first account of 'metallogeny' (the distribution of ore deposits in the crust) and noted that 'around 4000 BC in the country of Saones ...... the winter torrents brought down gold, which the barbarians collected in troughs pierced with holes and lined with fleeces'. No doubt Jason and his Argonauts on their famous voyage in 1200 BC came upon such mining operations where they were able to recover the 'golden fleece'. Strabo also commented on alluvial gold workings in places as far afield as Spain and Iran, and identified the areas where the deposits formed.

The Roman scholar Pliny the Elder (AD 23–79) also mentions the extraction of gold and, writing in AD77, noted that gold production from Spanish alluvial deposits was 200,000 oz a year. In the Middle Ages, early mineralogists such as the German Georg Bauer (1494–1555) (usually known by his Latinized name, Georgius Agricola) produced the first definitive texts on how to go about mineral exploration and exploitation (fig 40).

FINDING GOLD TODAY

Modern mineral exploration is now largely a scientific process, using a combination of geology (fig 41), geochemistry (fig 42) and geophysics to focus on the most favourable areas. Geological knowledge is applied so the explorers can target terrains where the most favourable rocks and geological structures occur that are known to contain gold in other regions (fig 41). This reflects the old saying in the mining industry: 'If you want to find elephants, go to elephant country'.

Geochemical analysis of rocks, soils and waters for gold itself, or for the so-called 'pathfinder elements' associated with the precious metal, help the explorer get closer to the gold deposit (fig 39). Pathfinder elements include antimony, arsenic, mercury, silver, and thallium, which are often found in greater concentration than the gold and may be easier (and hence often cheaper) to analyse chemically (fig 42).

Geophysical exploration investigates the physical properties of the ground where the ores may occur, using instruments that measure such parameters as magnetic susceptibility, electromagnetic conductivity and so on (page 26). This may help the explorers to focus on areas of abundant metallic minerals or anomalous responses that are similar to those seen in known gold deposits elsewhere.

GEOCHEMICAL EXPLORATION

The traditional method of exploration for gold is by washing gravels in rivers in order to locate fine particles of gold, which may lead the explorer to more substantial gold deposits farther upstream. This technique can be equally well applied to soils or weathered rock, both of which can be washed in running water. In places where gold is particularly rich, this form of washing is often modified by small-scale miners into a mining technique. Many types of shovel and sluice for working gravel have been described in the literature, from ancient times to the present day. Sometimes, small-scale prospectors use air instead of water to separate gold particles, in a process similar to the winnowing of grain to remove the worthless chaff.

Pharoic texts from 2500 BC show Egyptians 'panning' for gold in water. Throughout history, the distinctive dish-shaped gold prospector's pan has been the most commonly used tool for prospecting (page 13, fig 24). The pan appears to have been developed in West Africa before the arrival in 1471 of the Portuguese, who then exported the idea worldwide.

39 *Assayers at work in the laboratory of a Welsh gold mine in the 1930s.*

40 Illustration of gold sluicing from the 15th-century book De Re Metallica by the German mineralogist Agricola.

EXPLORATION

Since that time, the gold pan has been produced in various forms and made of a range of materials (ranging from wood or metal to modern plastics). Use of the gold pan exploits the behaviour of the high-density precious metal in moving water. In skilled hands, a few kilograms of gravel placed into a pan can be worked in the water, separating the dense minerals from less dense ones. The dramatic difference in relative density between gold (19.3) and quartz sand (2.56), which typically forms the bulk of river detritus, enables gold particles to be easily separated from other minerals. Simple counting of the gold grains, or 'colours', recovered in each pan of gravel gives the prospector a rough idea of the gold content of a particular river.

Modern explorers have become more sophisticated and nowadays analyse gravel samples for gold and other elements by chemical techniques, removing the variabilities in the panning techniques. One problem with panning is that very fine gold particles are easily lost from the pan, particularly by inexpert panners. Detection limits of new techniques such as instrumental neutron activation analysis (INAA) or bulk leach extractable gold (BLEG) sampling, in which several hundred grammes or even several kilogrammes of sample are analysed for gold, mean that gold can be detected at the parts per billion level, which is below the level at which gold may be found by panning. For the definition of gold ore

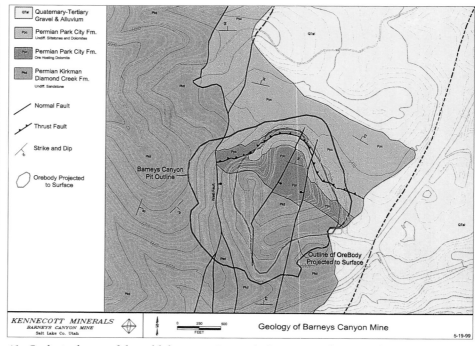

41 *Geological map of the gold deposit at Barney's Canyon, Utah, USA. The gold rich area is contained within the red line.*

that may be economically mined, companies still revert to the tried and tested fire assay analysis method (illustrated in fig 39). In fire assaying, the gold from the sample is extracted to form a tiny bead of the metal which can be physically weighed if need be guaranteeing the presence of gold in the sample.

GEOPHYSICAL SURVEYING

Geophysical surveying is a popular method of mineral exploration, as many of the methods can be employed using aircraft or even satellites and direct access to the ground may not be necessary at all. This 'remote sensing' clearly has many advantages for exploration in areas where access is difficult.

Gold is often located in veins, which follow fractures, or faults, in the rock. These faults can often be detected by subtle changes in magnetic field, so the use of detailed and precise magnetometer surveys may help pick them out. In many cases, the igneous magma bodies linked to the formation

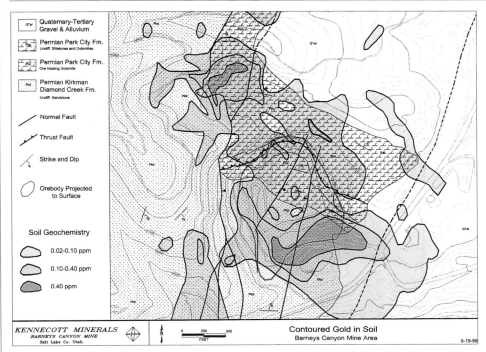

Legend

QTal	Quaternary-Tertiary Gravel & Alluvium
Ppc	Permian Park City Fm. Undiff. Siltstones and Dolomites
Ppc	Permian Park City Fm. Ore Hosting Dolomite
Pkd	Permian Kirkman Diamond Creek Fm. Undiff. Sandstone

Normal Fault

Thrust Fault

Strike and Dip

Orebody Projected to Surface

Soil Geochemistry

0.02-0.10 ppm

0.10-0.40 ppm

0.40 ppm

KENNECOTT MINERALS
BARNEYS CANYON MINE
Salt Lake Co. Utah

0   250   500
FEET

Contoured Gold in Soil
Barneys Canyon Mine Area

5-19-99

42 Geochemical map of the same area as fig 41, showing where gold is enriched in the soil over the gold ore-body.

of gold deposits in volcanic arcs contain magnetite, a magnetic iron-oxide mineral. Detailed magnetometer surveys can help locate these favourable bodies for closer investigation.

Alternatively, rocks close to gold deposits may be highly altered by the hydrothermal fluid, usually forming water-bearing minerals such as clay, mica and iron-bearing sulphides or oxides. This alteration leads to distinctive colour changes in the rocks, which can often be detected as 'colour anomalies' by airborne or satellite imaging surveys.

Micas and clay minerals (known as 'hydrous minerals') contain water and can be distinguished by their lower resistance to electrical currents than that of fresh rocks. Airborne electro-magnetic geophysical surveying, backed up by electrical resistivity measurements on the ground, can detect areas where these minerals may have formed. New portable instruments using infra-red technology can also detect the presence of these minerals, which form during hydrothermal activity related to the creation of the gold deposit.

DRILL TESTING

In the final analysis, mining cannot take place unless a satisfactory quantity (tonnage) and quality (grade) of the ore can be defined. This has to be done by taking representative samples of the rock, often by drilling (fig 43). Further exploration work may demand underground sampling or bulk testing. Samples collected must be analysed carefully for gold by reputable laboratories. In economic gold deposits, the gold is often invisible to the naked eye or even under a normal microscope, so fraudulent or erroneous claims have been common in the history of gold exploration. Gold can be easily introduced into samples as fine dust or in a dissolved form before analysis, so that even the laboratory may be unaware of the fraud (pages 50, 51).

43 Diamond-drilling rig exploring for copper-zinc-gold ore at Parys Mountain, Anglesey, North Wales, UK.

EXPLOITATION

PRODUCTION

Total world gold production to date is estimated to be in the order of 125,000 tonnes of metal, which, if cast as a solid block, would form a 19-metre cube. However, of this total, more than 90,000 tonnes has been produced since the European colonization of the Americas early in the 16th century.

Gold has been mined for thousands of years, with illustrations of Egyptian gold-working dating back to 2500 BC (fig 44) and Chinese gold production probably starting during the Shang Dynasty (4000 years ago). The Romans mined gold extensively, initially in Italy but then mainly in Spain, Portugal and Africa. Peak production may have provided as much as 5–10 tonnes of metal per year.

Placer gold was worked by pre-Colombian native Indian civilizations in the Andes from 1200 BC onwards. In Europe, gold production declined through the Dark and Middle Ages, increasing only with the Renaissance and the rise of colonialism from the 15th century onwards.

In the middle of the 15th century, significant gold was being produced in West Africa from the Gold Coast (now Ghana). The 16th-century conquests by the Spanish explorers of Mexico and Peru, and the later colonization of Brazil, by the Portuguese, opened up a new supply of gold. As a result of these two great sources of gold, one in the Old World and one in the New, total world production reached about 12 tonnes per year during the 17th century.

Towards the end of the 18th century, after discovery of alluvial gold in the Urals, Russia became a significant producer, mining up to 35 tonnes of gold annually by 1847 (when the world production stood at 75 tonnes). By 1914, Russian production had risen to 60 tonnes.

During the second half of the 19th century, several major gold rushes fuelled the rise in production. Three years after the start of the California Gold Rush in 1848, California produced 77 tonnes of gold, rising to 93 tonnes in 1853.

The Australian gold rushes led to a peak of 95 tonnes of gold produced in 1856 (when world production was 280 tonnes). During the 1860s, gold was sought in New Zealand, where the river systems of Otago and the West Coast of South Island have to date yielded over 600 tonnes of gold.

Then in, 1886, major gold deposits were discovered in South Africa, which rapidly became the most significant source of gold on earth. South Africa production peaked in 1970 when 1000 tonnes of gold was produced. In 1893 gold deposits were found at Kalgoorlie, Western Australia, yielding over 1200 tonnes of gold to date.

The last gold rush of the 19th century was to the Yukon, Canada, where between 1896 and 1899 the alluvial

44 Workers polishing gold and silver vases, painting in Rekhmire's Tomb, Egypt, 1552–1305 BC.

45 A bucket dredger being used for processing of gold-bearing gravels in the Yukon, Canada.

deposits of the Klondike produced some 75 tonnes of gold, when world gold production was about 400 tonnes per annum.

GOLD PRODUCTION IN THE 20TH CENTURY

In the 20th century, gold production dwindled until a final relaxation of the fixing of dollar prices to a gold standard in 1978. In the 1980s, gold price and production boomed, to reach world output of about 2000 tonnes in 1990.

New, rich alluvial gold deposits were exploited by small-scale miners. For example, the deposit of Serra Palada in Brazil, worked entirely by small-scale miners known as *garimpeiros*, produced over 10 tonnes of gold in 1983 alone.

Major mining companies explored worldwide for further deposits, with new gold-mining booms in established gold-producing areas such as Australia, Canada, the USA and South America. In addition, major exploration efforts were

46 South African miners drilling at the face deep underground at the Venterspost gold mine in the Witwatersrand.

focused on new gold-rich areas around the Pacific rim, notably Indonesia and the Philippines.

Today, about 2500 tonnes of gold is produced annually in more than 50 countries, although this is dominated by only about ten of these. Nowadays, mining solid rock yields most of this total, although the alluvial deposits of the former Soviet Union, China and Latin America are still important contributors.

TABLE 3. GOLD PRODUCTION FIGURES FOR 1998

South Africa	475 tonnes
USA	365 tonnes
Latin America	335 tonnes
Australia	315 tonnes
Canada	165 tonnes
China	160 tonnes
Indonesia	140 tonnes
Russia	125 tonnes
Uzbekistan	80 tonnes
Ghana	75 tonnes
Papua New Guinea	65 tonnes

EXTRACTION

Through all of pre-history and most of history, the bulk of gold has been recovered mechanically by hand as free grains, from either unconsolidated gravel or easily crushed rock. It was in New Zealand that steam-powered, bucket-line dredges were first pioneered in the 1880s. From there they were exported first to the USA and then to the Urals of Russia to mechanize the extraction of alluvial gold (fig 45).

Alluvial gold is by its nature free, so gravity separation is the common method of gold recovery. When the gold is concentrated by gravity methods, it may then be separated from other dense minerals, such as iron or titanium oxides and silicate minerals, by magnetic and electrostatic separators.

47 *Evidence of Roman gold workings at Dolaucothi mine, Central Wales, UK.*

However, since Roman times at least, gold has also been recovered from hardrock deposits. Simple hardrock gold ores that are called 'free-milling' may, like alluvial gold, need only gravity separation after crushing. This is a very cheap recovery method. Even mines that employ more complex recovery methods for the gold often have a simple gravity circuit ahead of more complex treatment in order to recover the portion of the gold that is free-milling more cheaply.

Over time, the target size for economic gold deposits has become larger, reflecting economies of scale in extraction technologies, and conversely the amount of gold contained in a given volume of typical ore (its grade) has decreased, reflecting similar advances in extraction technology. In modern open-pit mines, extractable ore grades have in some cases dropped to only about 1 g per tonne of gold (fig 49). Despite this, most gold deposits contain at least some relatively coarse gold, which can be removed by gravity methods and concentrated before the remaining material is subject to other concentrating techniques (fig 50).

MERCURY AMALGAMATION

From early times, people observed that mercury could be used to form an amalgam with fine gold grains. In about 300 BC, the Greek philosopher Theophrastus first described a method of mercury amalgamation of gold that

enabled fine gold to be recovered more effectively from concentrated mineral sands. Theophilus, an 11th-century German monk, described in some detail the washing of Rhine gravels on tables, with the later recovery of gold using mercury amalgamation.

The technique of gravity recovery, coupled with mercury amalgamation and subsequent separation, was the dominant extraction technology until relatively recently for both alluvial and hard rock gold deposits. Until the introduction of the cyanide method of gold extraction in the late 18th century, the more complex vein ores were treated by the use of Cornish-designed stamp mills combined with mercury amalgamation.

CYANIDE EXTRACTION

In 1843 the German chemist Bagration discovered that gold readily dissolved in alkaline cyanide solution. The famous British chemist and physicist Michael Faraday carried out further experiments to confirm this, which led the British chemists John S. MacArthur and the brothers Robert and William Forrest to develop the MacArthur-Forrest gold cyanidation process and patent it in 1889. Gold could be recovered from the cyanide solution by treatment with finely divided zinc metal. In the late 1890s, this technique was applied to lower-grade gold ores from the Witwatersrand, South Africa, to great effect. Although the method had early problems, the use of cyanide in gold extraction from low-grade ores has revolutionized gold mining in many areas of the world.

LEACHING TECHNIQUES

The use of cyanide blossomed in the 1970s with the development of so-called 'heap-leaching' technology, which was specifically aimed at recovering gold from the new reserves of low-grade gold ores being discovered in Nevada, USA, and Australia, as well as low-grade waste material dumped from previous mining. After the ore has been mined, it is carefully stacked into heaps on top of an impermeable liner (made of plastic, cement or some similar material). Next, a dilute cyanide solution (0.05 to 0.2 weight percent of sodium cyanide, NaCN) is passed through hoses onto the top of the heap, where it is trickled over the ore via a sprinkler system. Other

reagents, such as lime, are often added to keep the cyanide solution stable. After leaching the ore, the cyanide solution containing the dissolved gold runs out of the bottom of the heap (fig 48).

Only certain ores are amenable to heap leaching, however. Other, more complex, ores are treated either by grinding the ore in a solution of cyanide or by leaching it in tanks, where the ore and cyanide solution are agitated.

The gold must then be removed from the cyanide solution. In the past, this was done by reacting the leach solution with powdered zinc metal, using a technique called the Merrill-Crowe process. The gold then forms a slurry that can be removed. More modern methods – carbon in pulp (CIP), carbon in leach (CIL) or carbon in columns (CIC) – use activated carbon, which is added to the leach solution to adsorb the gold from the cyanide (that is, to

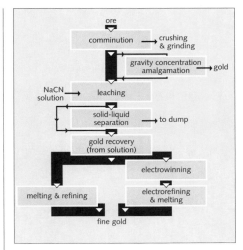

50 Flow-chart showing extraction of gold from ore.

take up the gold and deposit it on the surface of the carbon as a thin film). The carbon is then removed from the solution and treated to recover the gold.

Other reagents, in addition to cyanide, may have a future in gold processing. Chlorine has been used for low-sulphide ores and the similar element bromine is very efficient at dissolving gold. Thiourea also dissolves gold from some ores and may become more widely used, since it is far less toxic than cyanide.

ELECTROWINNING

A process called 'electrowinning', developed in 1950 by the American mining chemist Zadra, uses a special electrolytic cell full of steel wool to precipitate the gold from the cyanide.

48 A cyanide heap-leach pad and sprinkler system at Barney's Canyon, Utah, USA.

49 Large scale open-pit mining at Morro do Ouro, Brazil where gold ore with as little as 0.5 g gold per tonne is mined.

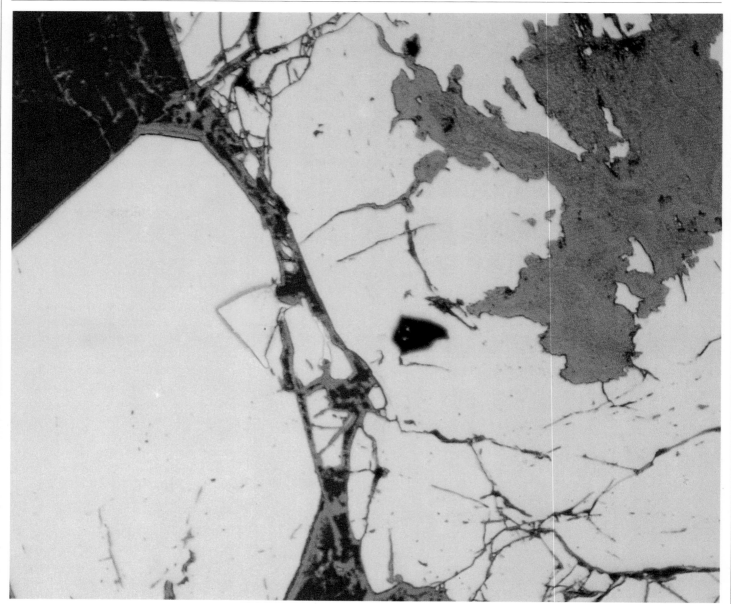

51 *Gold grain partially encapsulated by a pyrite grain.*

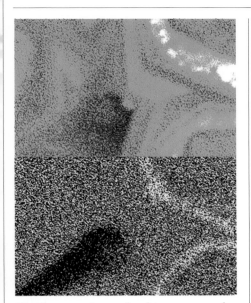

52 *Electron microprobe element maps of pyrite showing copper (above) and gold (below) levels in the mineral. In the lower image the bright bands show gold present at a concentration of around 0.2% within the mineral (width of images 500 μm).*

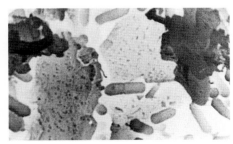

53 *Electron micrograph of bio-leaching process: the 5 μm long rod-shaped bacteria* Thiobacillus ferrooxidans *thrive among the sulphide mineral grains, which they break down, releasing trapped gold.*

The steel wool is then removed and the gold recovered. This is a cheaper method than using zinc.

Gold ores that are not directly amenable to this cheap cyanidation are referred to as refractory ores. Such ores may need prior treatment, as they may contain minerals, such as clays, carbon minerals or complex sulphide minerals, that inhibit gold extraction. The ore may be pre-treated to remove such problem constituents. For example, roasting it in air removes sulphides and carbon minerals.

INVISIBLE GOLD

In addition to gold in the native state or gold tied up in tellurium-, selenium- or sulphur-bearing minerals, sometimes much of the gold in an ore appears hidden in other minerals. In such cases, gold is found in the minerals as sub-microscopic particles, as a colloid, locked up in the mineral structure with pyrite (FeS_2), arsenopyrite (FeAsS) or some other such mineral. This type of gold is referred to as invisible gold.

Advanced analytical techniques are needed to determine the presence of invisible gold, including Mossbauer spectroscopy, secondary ion mass spectrometry, and electron microprobe element mapping (fig 52). Because the gold is locked within other minerals, it must first be liberated from the mineral within which it is trapped before it can be extracted, using pressure oxidation, roasting or biological methods.

Pressure oxidation involves sealing sulphide ores in solution in a reaction vessel known as an autoclave and then passing oxygen over them at high temperature. As the sulphide matrix is altered, gold atoms are liberated. They can then be leached with cyanide solutions.

Roasting of the ore, using fluidized bed furnaces, is another technique for extracting gold from refractory ores, but unless the sulphurous and arsenious fumes are cleaned in some way, the surrounding area could become polluted.

BIOLOGICAL METHODS

Bacteria have recently been used to oxidize complex ores before cyanidation, in a technique known as bioleaching that was pioneered in South Africa. The bacteria feed on the sulphide minerals, in the process releasing trapped gold, which then becomes available for cyanide dissolution. The strange rod-shaped bacterium *Thiobacillus ferrooxidans*, which thrives in extremely acidic environments, is sometimes used in the processing of refractory or 'invisible' gold ores (fig 53). Careful control of conditions is necessary for success.

More recently, scientists have raised the prospect of 'phytomining', using plants such as Chinese mustard (*Brassica juncea*) that accumulate gold in their vegetation, as a possible viable extraction method for gold in low-grade surface ores.

GOLD MINING AND THE ENVIRONMENT

Since early times, gold extraction of all types, has, to some degree, had a detrimental effect on the environment. Rock is moved around, quarries, pits and trenches are dug, rivers are diverted or disturbed, and habitats may be destroyed. In this way, whole ecosystems may be affected. In most cases, this disturbance is usually only for the duration of actual mining and for some years afterwards until, as nature takes its course, such operations become overgrown and revert more or less to the original state.

In some cases, however, the physical effects of mining are less than the chemical legacy of poorly controlled operations. Chemical pollution of the environment may arise where processing of the extracted ore has occurred. Four of the most problematic pollution sources resulting from mining are described below.

ACID ROCK DRAINAGE

Gold is often associated with the common sulphides pyrite and arsenopyrite, which may be discarded as waste.

However, if left untreated, dumps of these sulphides can react on exposure to the atmosphere to form acidic waters. This acid water can cause serious pollution of river courses and buried aquifers if it escapes.

MERCURY POLLUTION

Because the metal mercury readily amalgamates with gold, it was widely used in the past for the final stages of gold extraction. Major mining companies replaced mercury in their extraction technologies long ago, but

54 *Smoke pours from the chimney of the Deadwood and Delaware gold smelter, Deadwood, South Dakota, 1890.*

55 *An artesanal gold miner displays mercury recovered from a polluted river in the Philippines.*

for many small-scale miners, particularly in developing countries, mercury is still the method of choice to recover gold from fine sands. Many of the *garimpeiros* in the Amazon basin of South America amalgamate the gold from their concentrate in a bucket with water from the river. Some mercury is lost during this washing and more (about 20%) is lost when the resulting gold-mercury amalgam is heated until the mercury vaporizes, dispersing the toxic element widely into the environment.

It was estimated that about 100 tonnes of mercury was polluting the Brazilian Amazon annually during the 1980s. Mercury is an element that is toxic to many animals and also to humans. Moreover, it remains unaltered for a long time in river sediments, so it can be hazardous to human health well after the mining has stopped. It accumulates in fish, molluscs, and crustaceans, from where it continues up the food chain to become concentrated in animal predators – and humans.

CYANIDE SPILLAGE

Sodium cyanide is now widely used in processes to extract gold. Enough is known about the toxicity of cyanide to humans and animals for the mining industry to take the utmost care in its use and devise closed systems that do not pollute ground or surface waters. Although highly toxic, cyanide rapidly breaks down in the natural environment to harmless compounds and thus does not create the long-term pollution problems of substances such as mercury.

ARSENIC POLLUTION

When gold occurs together with or inside arsenopyrite, especially when it is refractory and not amenable to conventional processing technology, roasting of the ore may be used to break down the ore. This may lead to arsenic vapour being released from the chimney of the smelter, polluting the surrounding land. For example, long-term arsenic pollution at the Ashanti gold mine processing plant in Ghana led to health

problems in the local community. Fortunately, modern upgrades to the plant have cut emissions to acceptable levels. Many similar operations in Eastern Europe, the former Soviet Union and Third World countries have left a legacy of pollution, which in some cases has been shown to reduce average human lifespan by a third, to lead to an increasing number of birth defects, and to compromise the health and well-being of the population for miles around.

56 *Modern gold-processing plant at Morro do Ouro, Brazil; plant also contains a water treatment and recycling facility.*

57 *Nursery at Morro do Ouro mine, showing indigenous trees and shrubs grown to test for use in rehabilitation when mining has been completed.*

POLLUTION AND THE LAW

In most countries, the law now requires environmental impact assessments before gold mining or any other extractive industrial operation can begin. These involve a thorough investigation of air quality, water quality, land disturbance and degradation, and the likely impacts on biodiversity and human health, as well as socio-economic factors. International mining groups are closely monitored by their shareholders and bankers who insist on strict observance of international guidelines for environmental control. Environmental monitoring takes place throughout the working life of such a mine or quarry, and may continue long after closure, with rehabilitation of the environment mandatory following mine closure.

THE GOLD RUSHES

Many of the major, successful searches for gold have been the result of almost accidental finds by lone prospectors (fossickers) or wanderers. Discoveries, or even merely the rumour of discoveries, led to the making of fortunes for some but hardship and deprivation for others. The gold rushes often involved mass migrations of populations, both from home and abroad, and were of course a significant influence on the economy and political framework of the local areas and countries involved.

People have sought gold continuously, from ancient times to the present day, in many parts of the world, but it was the New World that proved to be the first great gold-seeker's paradise. The conquistadores, the Spanish conquerors of the New World in the 16th century, were perhaps the first major influence on the worldwide search and on the exploitation of gold.

One of the most famous of these men, Hernando Cortés, uncovered the wealth of the Aztecs in Mexico in 1519. This spurred on others, such as Francisco Pizarro, who travelled south to Peru in search of Inca treasure. Atahualpa, the Inca ruler of Peru, was captured by Pizarro and ransomed for enough gold to fill the room that was his prison together with twice its volume in silver. Pizarro extracted some eight tonnes of gold from the Incas before proceeding to have Atahualpa strangled in 1533.

Gold production from the New World fuelled economic growth in Spain and Portugal. England was also able to prosper from this gold since much of it was 'liberated' by privateers and pirates at the behest of the English crown.

It was however much later, in the USA, that there occurred the first of the great, well-documented gold rushes that involved thousands of individuals in mass migrations, to remote and often inhospitable parts of the world.

THE GREATEST GOLD RUSH OF ALL TIME

Although the first nugget of gold to be discovered in the USA by settlers was found in North Carolina in 1799, and major gold strikes occurred in Georgia in 1825–29, it was to be California that witnessed the greatest of all the gold rushes.

James Marshall, from New Jersey, was at the beginning of 1848 in charge of the construction of a saw-mill at

58 *Spanish Conquistadores persecuting Peruvian tribespeople: engraving by Theodore de Bry (1528–1598).*

Coloma, on the South Fork of the American River, California. For this project he was the partner of John Augustus Sutter, a rich Swiss settler and landowner, living in a fortified community known as 'Sutters Fort'. On the morning of 24 January 1848, he was supervising the deepening of the mill-stream, when a yellowish object caught his eye. It proved to be gold, and many more pieces were found.

Eventually, this information filtered through to government officials and on 5 December 1848, President James Polk mentioned the find in his annual statement to Congress. This news travelled around the world and was to trigger the great California gold rush of 1849.

The finds were in frontier country, within the mountain streams and eastern foothills of the Sierra Nevada Range in the new state of California. It appeared to the prospectors – who soon became known as 'forty-niners' because most of them set off to seek their fortunes in 1849 – that gold seams occurred along vast tracts of this area. The streams running off the granite hills contained flakes and nuggets of gold. Prospectors sought the legendary 'Mother Lode', which was thought to be the primary source, and was said to stretch for more than 100 km and to be uniform in gold content. Although gold in the bedrock was found, the rush was largely fuelled by the alluvial riches.

LONG JOURNEYS

The rush was on, and people flocked to the area, from all continents (fig 59 . As a result, by the end of 1849, the population of California had risen from about 26,000 to 115,000. To get to the gold, the potential prospectors used a variety of routes. For many, the route was overland straight across the continent, north up the Missouri river by boat, and then back on dry land, following the Oregon and California trails.

The forty-niners travelled on horseback or by covered wagon, lurching along rough trails through remote, rugged landscapes. Europeans and Americans from the East Coast tended to undertake the extremely long sea journey around South America via Cape Horn, while Australians headed across the Pacific. Another shorter but extremely hazardous route was by sea and land across Panama and then northwards up to San Francisco.

BOOM-TIME

The prospectors and adventurers established mining camps throughout the region. Most of the forty-niners used a pick, pan or cradle and constructed sluices to control the flow of water in their claim. The Middle Fork of the American River was said to be the richest of the Great Valley streams, with up to 10,000 miners working its riches. Much of the life was rough and tough and 'claim-jumping' often occurred. Unofficial juries were set up to settle such disputes.

The prospectors welcomed the shout of "Colour!", meaning that a few flakes or maybe a nugget had been found. The largest single nugget, found at Carson Hill, was said to weigh 90 kg. Fortunes could be based on hard work or, simply, luck – it is said that some of the more fortunate forty-niners found gold under plants or literally stumbled over gold-bearing boulders.

In the decade after the first discovery, about US$500 million of gold was produced. The peak year was 1852 with some US$80 million of gold extracted. By the late 1850s, prosperity started to wane, as the finding and winning of gold

59 Poster advertising an American clipper ship, about 1850: vessels such as these enabled many of the 'forty-niners' to join the Californian gold rush.

THE GOLD RUSHES

60 Irish prospectors operating a 'Long Tom' sluice for washing gold dirt, California, 1849.

became harder. Mining continued, but slowly the miners began to leave, attracted by stories of new gold elsewhere. Famous discoveries were at the Comstock Lode in Nevada (1859), the Homestake Mine in South Dakota (1878) and Cripple Creek, Colorado (1891).

The great energy and enthusiasm of the Californian forty-niners was now over. Today, although gold is still won from the mines of California it is often not processed but instead ends up as outstanding museum and collectors' specimens (fig 2).

AUSTRALIAN GOLD RUSHES

Gold rushes were to dominate Australian life in the 1850s. Gold had been found in New South Wales as early as 1823, but it was not until the discovery by Edward Hargreaves in February 1851 of alluvial gold in the Macquarie River, near the town of Bathurst, just over 200 km west of Sydney, that the Australian gold-mining era started. Hargreaves had left Australia to join the California gold rush, but his prospecting was mostly unsuccessful. However, he had learnt from the experience, and returned to Australia to prospect remote, unmapped areas likely to contain gold. Hargreaves' discovery was subsequently dramatically reinforced when an Aborigine tending sheep stumbled across a quartz boulder containing some 27 kg of gold.

Alluvial gold was discovered later in 1851 by a local blacksmith in Victoria, leading to the establishment of the rich goldfields of Ballarat and Bendigo. Prospectors from all over the world began to flood into these areas (fig 61). The Australian gold rush was well and truly underway. Between 1851 and 1894 further major finds contributed to a 'golden trail', with an anti-clockwise trend around Australia. Rich nuggety gold with quartz was a feature of these early discoveries. It is believed that the largest mass of gold ever recovered from a 'quartz reef' was the Holterman Nugget found in the Hill End goldfield, New South Wales, in 1872. It weighed some 300 kg and probably contained 95 kg of gold, before processing.

61 The claim disputed, lithograph from Victoria gold diggings and diggers as they are, Samuel Thomas Gill, 1852.

FAMOUS FINDS

Some of the biggest and most famous nuggets were found in the state of Victoria. The largest of these was the Welcome Stranger, which contained 71 kg of gold (fig 62) (worth about US$600,000 at today's prices). It would have been worth two or three times this value if it had been saved as a specimen and not melted down. This nugget was uncovered in 1869 by the wheel of a passing wagon on a bush track in Black Head, Moliagul. The second largest was the Welcome Nugget (62.9 kg), found earlier, in 1858, on Bakery Hill, Ballarat, Victoria. A much smaller, but important nugget (0.65 kg) was found at the McIver Mount goldmine, Victoria, in 1835. This was named the Latrobe Nugget after the then Governor of the State of Victoria, Charles Latrobe. The importance of this nugget is that it is still considered to be the best formed

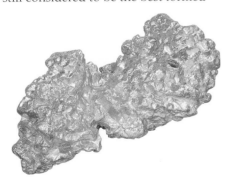

62 Model of the 'Welcome Stranger' nugget, at a weight of 78 kg the largest gold nugget ever found anywhere: the actual nugget was melted down to yield 71 kg of pure gold.

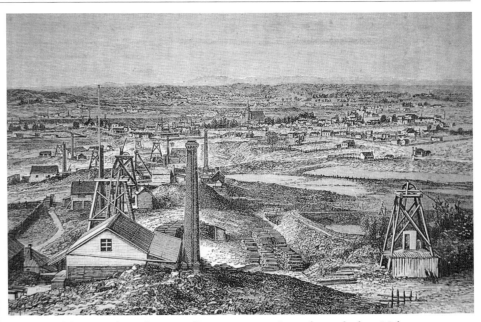

63 The gold mines of Sandhurst, Ballarat, Victoria, Australia in the late 19th century.

crystallized gold known, the whole mass being formed of gold cubes (fig 6).

In recent times, around some of the old gold-mining areas, for example in Victoria and the Kalgoorlie area of Western Australia, some sizeable nuggets have been recovered, sometimes with the help of metal-detectors. One of the largest is the 'Hand of Faith' nugget from Victoria (27 kg).

In 1898, Kalgoorlie was the leading gold production area in Australia, but by the early 1900s, the gold rushes were over and a long decline in production had set in. By 1953 however, Australian gold production had climbed again, to reach over 28 tonnes. By the late 1980s, gold production had almost quadrupled, with annual production then standing at over 100 tonnes.

SOUTH AFRICA – 'THE RAND'

There are records of gold being worked from various localities in Africa throughout historical times. This is particularly true in West Africa, but it is South Africa that rose to become the world's leading gold producer. Before European settlers arrived, indigenous people mined gold in Africa, largely for ornamental purposes. The presence of gold in West Africa led explorers inland to southern Africa and gold was located

THE GOLD RUSHES

in the Transvaal and in what is now Zimbabwe. By far the most important occurrence of gold is in the area known as the Witwatersrand, which early explorers overlooked in their haste to reach the legendary riches in Africa's interior. To date the Witwatersrand area has accounted for approximately 98% of all historical gold production in South Africa.

In 1834, Carel Kruger discovered gold in the Witwatersrand while on a hunting expedition. Little attention was paid to his find at this time, as other areas were already in production. There is some evidence that two brothers named Strueben had started small-scale mining in 1885 on one of the farms in the region.

LUCKY FINDS
In 1886, George Harrison, who had been an Australian gold digger, discovered gold while chipping stones to build a home. However, a more famous and momentous event also happened in the same year, when George Walker, a handyman, reputedly tripped over a rock in a field on the Langlaagte farm in the Witwatersrand region. The rock proved to be gold-bearing, and the 'Rand', as this area became known, proved to have extensive gold bearing 'reefs'.

Walker's find started a gold rush, although this was somewhat different from that in other countries in that

64 South African goldworkers in the Wiwatersrand, 1990s.

65 The thriving city of Johannesburg today, with dumps from the gold mines visible in the background.

diamond mining was already active at Kimberley, so that a framework of organization was already in place. Gold licences were soon being issued to work claims of about 100 acres – the fee for a five-year lease was 10 shillings a month.

The 'gold reefs' of the Rand often dipped steeply from the surface, so that underground mining proved to be necessary at almost the earliest stage. This easily mined conglomerate passed into harder, more sulphide-rich ore, from which it became more difficult to recover the gold. However, technology was developed to exploit these ores and the region has grown to become the single most important gold-producing area in the world, still yielding some 500 tonnes of gold per annum, centred on the large city of Johannesburg (figs 64, 65).

THE KLONDIKE GOLD RUSH

This was perhaps the last great gold rush. It was certainly one of the most arduous and demanding, and for many of the prospectors it turned out to be a fruitless search. The gold-rush area was in the remote, rugged landscape of Yukon Territory, western Canada. Here the summers are hot but the winters extremely harsh, with very low temperatures and deep snow.

To the west, the neighbouring state of Alaska had been settled by the Russians since 1741 but then sold to the United States in 1867. Gold had been found in modest quantities in several rivers of the region. During the late 1880s and into the 1890s, prospectors moving north from California to try their luck ventured across the ill-defined US/Canada border. Soon, new and major gold discoveries were being made along the great Yukon river that flowed through Canada's Yukon Territory into Alaska, and in its associated tributaries, streams and creeks.

It all began in the summer of 1896, when Robert Henderson, a Canadian from Nova Scotia, was prospecting the Thron Diuck River in the Yukon. This was soon mispronounced by miners so that it came to be known as the Klondike River. In one of the tributaries Henderson found alluvial gold, and named the area Gold Bottom Creek. Another prospector, George Carmack from San Francisco (together with his Indian companions), learned of the find from Henderson, and they soon started exploring other areas in the vicinity. Somewhat by accident, on 16 August 1896, they stumbled upon sand riddled with small gold nuggets, at a site that became known as Bonanza Creek. For various reasons – not least the isolation of the area – the news took more than a year to leak to the outside world. The Klondike gold rush had begun.

GOLD FEVER

Gold seekers of every vocation converged on the region from all continents. Routes into the gold area were at times impassable, with rivers frozen in winter.

Those that could afford it took boats from California, landed on the Alaska coast and then climbed through the snow-covered Chilkoot and White passes (fig 67). After this exhausting experience, they still faced a 1000-km trek northwest. All food,

66 Outfitters' store for the Yukon prospectors, Vancouver, Canada, 1897.

67 Looking down Cutoff Canyon from the White Pass on the Chilkoot Trail, Yukon, Canada, 1898.

THE GOLD RUSHES

68 *Dawson city today, a shadow of its former self – the opposite of Johannesburg.*

equipment and stores had to be carried out and crates and sacks of gold were carried back south.

Gold fever next infected Dawson City, the main supply town for the goldfields. In a short time, the population of this boomtown mushroomed from a few hundred to 10,000 (fig 68).

Because of the climate, mining techniques had to be changed from summer to winter. During summer, the miners 'panned' the creeks, but they were forced to improvise during the winter by melting the thick layer of frozen soil, or permafrost, by lighting fires. If this technique was properly carried out, the bedrock was revealed and could be worked.

During the period 1899–1904, US$100 million of Klondike gold was produced. After these dates production started to decline, and prospectors started to go back west to new finds in Alaska. For the Klondike 'Stampeders', this was the end of the toughest gold rush of them all.

THE FORGOTTEN 'GOLD RUSH'

Although the steppes of southern Siberia were home to the ancient Scythians who worked gold, production was neglected until the sixteenth century conquest of Siberia by Russian explorers. Peter the Great abolished the state monopoly on mining, and in 1744 the Berezovsk gold mine was discovered close to Yekaterinburg in the eastern foothills of the Urals. This gold mine is still in production today, producing gold from thin gold veins in the metamorphic rocks.

Discovery of large placer deposits came later, with a change in the law in 1812 that allowed landowners to work their own minerals. Major deposits were discovered in the Urals in 1814, followed by discoveries farther east in the Altai Mountains in 1830. In 1836, large placer deposits were found along the Yenisey River. This led to a great rise in gold production, and by 1842, the governor general of eastern Siberia recorded the working of 58 alluvial gold deposits yielding some 10.8 tonnes per year of gold.

Further goldfields were found in the Lake Baikal and Amur regions in the far

eastern parts of Siberia during the 1850s and 1860s. This early gold mining never led to the kind of gold rushes seen in the USA or Australia. Many of the potentially suitable workers for the goldfields were held in serfdom in central Russia and were therefore not free to travel. However, the 1861 emancipation of serfs and the abolition of a gold tax in 1877 (which had reached 32% in 1849!) led to a sort of gold rush, reflected by a boom in gold production, which reached 43 tonnes per year by 1880.

Nevertheless, labour for the Siberian gold mining industry was underpinned by exiles and political offenders. Conditions were harsh, with long cold winters and short, hot summers plagued by mosquitoes and blackflies. In 1889 changes in the law allowed mine-owners to buy in foreign technology and the Trans-Siberian railway opened up the region for transportation.

Gold production grew until 1914, when it reached nearly 2 million oz of gold annually. In 1914 the revolution ended all entrepreneurial efforts and mining passed once more back to the state. Gold production under the Soviets expanded to a peak production in 1988 of 190 tonnes, largely from the great alluvial gravel deposits of Siberia. Currently, gold production in Russia has dropped to about 120 tonnes per year.

69 *The Lena goldfield, eastern Siberia, Russia, showing the low-technology nature of the mining, about 1912.*

GOLD IN THE UNITED STATES

Only South Africa produces more gold than the USA, where annual production stands at more than 330 tonnes per annum. A large proportion of the US production is as a by-product of other metal mining operations, particularly copper. The belt of large porphyry copper deposits that runs through Utah, Arizona and New Mexico accounts for more than 80 tonnes of gold annually. The largest of these, the huge porphyry copper deposit of Bingham Canyon in Utah, alone produces almost 20 tonnes of gold per year.

The state of Nevada is a particularly important gold producer, accounting for some 210 tonnes annually, most of which comes from epithermal and sediment-hosted gold deposits. Nevada is the home of the distinctive Carlin deposits, which produce some 45 tonnes each year from a series of deposits in a linear belt 50 km long. Other major deposits in Nevada include the epithermal deposits of Round Mountain, Paradise Peak and other sediment-hosted deposits, such as Twin Creeks.

The Homestake mine in South Dakota, which has been producing gold since 1876, still yields over 12 tonnes of gold per year. This deposit occurs in highly folded, 1.7-billion-year-old, iron-rich metamorphic rocks.

Alaska, Arizona, California, Colorado, Montana and Washington also yield significant quantities of gold from a variety of gold deposit types, including all those described earlier. Despite all this production, the US consumption of gold for jewellery and manufacturing still exceeds annual domestic production by a ratio of two or more to one.

GOLD IN EUROPE

Current gold production for Europe is about 25 tonnes of gold per annum. However, Europe has been a gold producer since prehistoric times, with the earliest mining recorded in Thrace and other areas around the Aegean.

Many of these deposits are of the epithermal type and these areas are currently being re-evaluated in the light of new low-cost technology that may lead to increased production for Europe. New mines are likely to be developed in Greece and Turkey, close to regions with historic gold production.

In addition to these areas, epithermal gold deposits are mined in Romania, Bulgaria and Italy. Romania has been a significant mining region in the past, particularly during the 18th and 19th centuries, when it was part of the Austro-Hungarian Empire. By-product gold is recovered from porphyry copper mining in Serbia, Macedonia and Romania, and important historical gold-producing areas are also located in Slovakia and the Czech Republic.

In Spain, gold is recovered from sulphide ores formed at ancient black smokers (page 20), many of which have been upgraded by eluvial processes (page 12). Gold veins in the Massif Central and Montagne Noire of France have been large gold producers in the past, where all the major mines are now reaching the end of their lives.

Sweden and Finland recover gold as a by-product of mining copper ores, and many new deposits associated with metamorphic rocks have been discovered by recent exploration efforts in Scandinavia.

70 Blasted gold ore at the McLaughlin mine, California.

71 Ancient mining site, Las Medulas, Spain.

GOLD IN USA/EUROPE

GOLD IN THE BRITISH ISLES

Gold has been discovered in the British Isles at intervals since pre-Roman times. Even though it occurs only in minor amounts in comparison to some of the world's major gold belts, significant finds of gold are reported from a variety of terrains throughout the British Isles. Gold is usually found as small flakes or nuggets in alluvial deposits, mostly associated with the older, underlying rocks of England, Wales, Ireland and Scotland. Recently there has been increased prospecting activity, leading to significant discoveries in Scotland and Ireland, and in Devon, South West England.

WALES

In terms of known production, the richest gold-mining area in the British Isles was centred on North Wales. Several mines were worked in this area from about 1840, the gold found there being mainly associated with Cambrian slates. The gravels of the River Mawddach have yielded flakes and small nuggets. Two of the mines, Clogau-St Davids and Gwynfynydd, were worked until recently (fig 72). Traditionally, gold from the Clogau-St Davids mine has been used in wedding rings for the British Royal Family.

The hey-day for these mines was in the early 1860s and although some production has continued over the years, the discovery of rich finds has been only spasmodic. Output from the mines of the Dolgellau area reached its peak in 1904.

To the north east of Gwynfynydd, the Castell Carndochan mine, near Bala, worked gold in quartz veins, cutting volcanic rocks. The mine produced nearly 50 kg of gold between 1863 and 1865.

In South Wales it is believed that the Ogofau mine was worked for gold by the Romans. Recent working has had only limited success but Ogofau serves as a teaching mine for the University of Wales and is open as a museum.

SCOTLAND

Gold has been found at many locations in Scotland, mostly in alluvial deposits, but recent discoveries have been in vein deposits. The first record of gold in the alluvial deposits of Scotland dates back to the 13th century. The country has produced interesting small nuggets and even had its own 'mini-goldrush'.

In the early part of the 19th century a single nugget weighing over 15 g was found in Helmsdale Water. Some years later, in 1868, a Mr R Gilchrist returned to Strath Kildonan after several years spent working in the Australian goldfields. He started prospecting and found gold associated with the tributaries of the Helmsdale River.

By April 1869, it is thought that there were some 500 prospectors in the area, working the alluvial deposits, especially in the Suisgill and Kildonan rivers. Every digger paid 10% royalty to the Duke of Sutherland and a licence fee of £1 per month. The Kildonan 'gold rush' is said to have produced about 93 kg of gold in just two years.

One of the earliest worked areas was centred on the Leadhills–Wanlockhead area of Dumfriesshire. Gold was first discovered here in the 16th century and much of the gold coinage of James V of Scotland (1513–1542) was mined from this area. To the north-east on Crawford Moor several nuggets were found including one of 930 g. Today all mining has ceased but enthusiasts still pan Wanlock Water.

72 A 62 g gold nugget recovered from Clogau, Wales.

73 The Breadalbane nugget, Scotland.

The headwaters of the Tay in Perthshire produced several interesting nuggets. The most famous of these was the Breadalbane nugget found in 1828, a mass with quartz said to contain 62 g of gold (fig 73).

Recently, economic gold has been found associated with related mineralization at Cononish near Tyndrum. It is hoped that the latter discovery will lead to a working mine.

IRELAND
Gold ornaments are known in Ireland from the early years of the Christian era. Torcs (twisted necklaces – fig 74), dating from the Bronze-Age are world-famous. These may or not be of local origin but it is known that in the

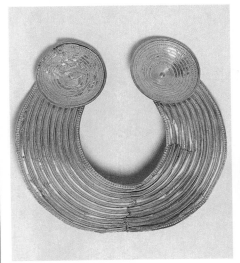

74 Irish gold and repoussé torc, from about 7th century BC.

18th century small nuggets were recovered from the Ballin valley stream, Co. Wicklow. This area was to prove the most important gold area in Ireland and from the alluvial deposit came the largest nugget found in the British Isles. This, the Wicklow nugget, was found in the Ballin valley stream in 1795 and became the property of George III. The nugget weighed 682 g (fig 75).

Recent prospecting by international mining companies has led to several

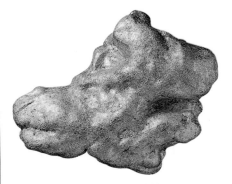

75 The Wicklow nugget, 682 g.

76 A view across the Wicklow Hills, a major gold-bearing area in Ireland.

discoveries of gold within the Caledonian terrains of Ireland, at such localities as Lack, Croag Patrick and Curraghinalt. Trial mining was carried out at Curraghinalt.

ENGLAND
In South West England, many of the streams worked for alluvial tin produced a few small flakes or rarely nuggets of gold. The largest recorded nugget of about 62 g was found in the headwater of Restronguet Creek, Perranworthal, Cornwall. Abundant alluvial gold has been recovered from the Treore stream, Port Isaac, also in Cornwall. In North Devon, the old copper mines around North Molton, especially the Britannia and Bampylde mines contained some gold. Gold has also been found associated with antimony, arsenic and copper ores in east-west veins.

However, the best known gold specimens from South West England have come from Hopes Nose, a small headland situated east of Torquay, South Devon. Here, fine dendritic gold sprays have been found associated with calcite veins in Devonian shales (fig 5). Recent surveys have shown gold to be widely distributed in the drainage channels and soils of the area.

Gold discoveries have recently been reported from the Crediton area of mid-Devon. It is present within the river system associated with Permian volcanic rocks.

GOLD IN ANTIQUITY

'The Assyrian came down like the wolf on the fold
And his cohorts were gleaming in purple and gold.'

Byron, *The Destruction of Sennacherib,*

Gold is one of the seven metals of antiquity, the others being copper, iron, lead, mercury, silver and tin. Together with the alloys bronze (copper and tin) and electrum (gold and silver), these metals formed the basis for metallurgy from early through to mediaeval times.

THE PALAEOLITHIC PERIOD
Throughout most of the Stone Age, there is no evidence that early humans were remotely interested in gold, although they would undoubtedly have come across it in alluvial accumulations in streams and at outcrops in the mountains. Being softer than the stone weapons at their disposal, gold was probably not prized for making weapons and its earliest uses were likely to have been entirely decorative. Indeed, there have been races throughout history that have simply ignored the gold in their native lands. The precious metal has played almost no part in Maori or Aborigine cultures, for instance, although it is naturally abundant in both New Zealand and Australia.

THE NEOLITHIC PERIOD
Few metal ornaments have been found in Neolithic sites (8000–4200 BC), but the world's oldest gold hoard, dated at

4600–4200 BC, was discovered in an ancient burial ground at Varna, Bulgaria, and can be regarded as early Bronze Age, or Chalcolithic (from the Greek word for copper, *khalkos*). These artefacts are testament to the advanced nature of the early Thracian civilization that flourished in the south-east corner of the Balkan peninsula at this time.

Probably, about 90% of the gold unearthed by archaeologists has been from hoards belonging to three general types: votive offerings to the various gods; burials of rulers and other high-status individuals; and the scrap-metal

stashes of goldsmiths. One of the possible exceptions to this is the treasure unearthed in the late 19th century from the ruins of Troy by the German archaeologist Heinrich Schliemann. This is now believed to date from about 2500 BC, although it was originally ascribed to King Priam, the much later King of Troy, who featured in Homer's *Iliad*.

Almost all the ancient civilizations emerging in the 2nd and 3rd millennia BC, from the Egyptian, through the Minoan, Mycenaean and Greek, to the Celtic, used gold in some form or other

77 *Gold plaque from a Scythian hoard, 4th century BC, Kul Oba, Russia.*

78 Pre-Colombian gold figure (1000–1500 BC), Quimbaya, Colombia.

and revered it. Amazing artistic talent, probably introduced by Greek settlers, is revealed, even within so-called 'barbaric' cultures, such as that of the Scythians, who occupied the Eurasian steppes between Ukraine and Mongolia from the 7th to the 3rd centuries BC (fig 77). Similarly, another group of largely nomadic peoples, the Bactrians, who inhabited what is now Afghanistan during the 1st century BC, produced remarkable gold artefacts.

Peruvian civilizations, too, valued gold highly, and worked alluvial deposits in the Andes from the 12th century BC onwards. The Chavin people and other pre-Colombian cultures, such as that of the Nazca, developed goldsmithing to a fine art (fig 78). This culminated in the Chimu Empire of northern Peru, which climaxed prior to the European invasion. Techniques such as wire rolling and gold plating were developed by them, as also was that of lost-wax casting (*cire perdue*). In this technique, a model is made of wax, then covered in clay, which is allowed to set. The molten gold is then poured through a small hole left in the clay mould onto the wax, which vaporizes, so that the gold replaces it and fills the mould.

COINAGE

Gold had a value in the ancient world. For instance, in the code of Menes, the first king of the first dynasty of Egypt in 3100 BC, one part of gold was declared equal in value to two-and-a-half parts of silver. Despite this, there is little evidence of the use of gold in coinage until late Greek or early Roman times, although it was certainly traded. Silver and copper were used for coinage at first and the earliest use of gold in coins as the gold-silver alloy electrum appears to have been in about 700 BC, in the Lydian-Ionian region of Greece. King Croesus had separate gold and silver coins minted in about 500 BC, the gold coins – known as 'staters', from the Greek *stater*, a standard of weight – containing about 8 g of gold.

By the middle of the first century BC, Roman currency had become trimetallic, using alloys of gold, silver and copper. Roman gold mining expanded at this time as new sources of the metals were sought. The *aureus denarius*, or 'gold penny', was in circulation for 300 years until about AD 250, and, after one of the reforms of the Emperor Constantine the Great around AD 300, a new smaller *aureus*, the *solidus*, made of pure unalloyed gold, was struck. This remained in circulation for some 1000 years in Byzantium. Eventually, in about AD 1000, even the *solidus* was debased to the extent that it contained only about one-third gold and two-thirds other metals.

79 An eight-drachma gold piece, showing Ptolomey II Philadelphus, King of Egypt 283–246 BC and his wife Arsinoe.

GOLD AS A COMMODITY

'They wonder much to hear that gold which in itself is so useless a thing should be everywhere so much esteemed'
Sir Thomas More

Today, gold is a commodity that can be openly bought and sold in the form of bars of metal (bullion), or as coins. Gold prices are traditionally fixed in US$ per troy ounce (31.1g) of metal. Its value in this form is much higher than either its industrial or decorative uses can support, since the metal hoarded by central banks as a reserve asset gives gold a so-called 'intrinsic' value.

CENTRAL BANKS

In the past, in times of war or currency collapse, gold had status, maintaining its value, so it could be used as collateral. In the past, the gold holdings of a country's central bank have given confidence to investors and creditors. Today, the central banks and other institutions hold about 35,000 tonnes of gold. This earns no interest, and in the period February 1996 to December 1998 decreased in value by about a third, as gold prices declined. It is not surprising, then, that even a major gold-producing country such as Australia sold some of its central bank holdings in 1998, risking the wrath of the gold-mining industry, since its action forced prices down. Further uncertainties in the gold market were caused in 1999 with the announcement by the UK that it would sell half its gold reserve (fig 80).

81 A stack of one-kilogramme gold bars of 99.99% purity.

A part of this decrease in the price of gold might be attributed to a weak market brought about by central-bank selling. But, just as the withdrawal of silver from use as currency led to a long-term decrease in the price of silver at the end of the last century, a similar decline may occur for gold. At the time of writing, the greatest gold hoarders are the USA, with 8150 tonnes; Germany, with 3700 tonnes; France, with 3200 tonnes; and Switzerland with 2590 tonnes.

When the price of gold peaked at US$850 per troy oz in January 1980, much of the useful and decorative gold was traded in and became valuable once more just for being gold.

TRADING

Gold is traded as bullion, the price being fixed twice daily on the London Bullion Market. It can be bought or sold 'forward' (in advance of delivery or production), as a means of minimizing risk, to both mining companies and end-users.

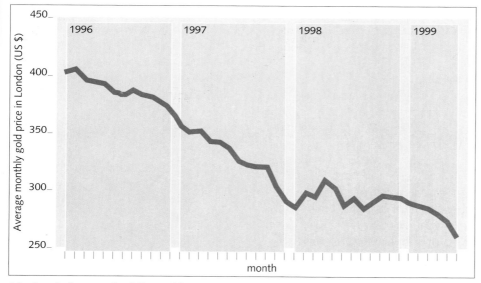

80 Graph showing the fall in gold prices.

However, a downside to this arrangement means that during times of low demand or oversupply, mines can continue to produce gold and be paid a higher price if they have sold their gold in advance. This forward selling contributes to the excess of supply over demand, and can prolong the period of low prices.

'Strive not for gold, for greedy fools measure themselves by poor men never Their standards still being richer men makes them poor ever.'

William Davies

According to the *Financial Times* of 30 January 1997, 30 million troy oz, or 930 tonnes, of gold, valued at more than US$10,000 million, is cleared through London, the international settlement centre for gold bullion, every working day. This represents nearly half the total annual global production of gold of about 2500 tonnes. In a bizarre, twice-daily ritual in an office at the bankers N M Rothschild & Sons Ltd, the chairman suggests an opening price, which is reported by five company representatives to their dealing rooms. The chairman then asks who wants to buy and who wants to sell and how many 400-oz bars they wish to trade. The price is moved up or down until there are matching amounts to be bought and sold. When a dealer is satisfied, a tiny Union Jack on his desk is lowered. When all five minature flags are down, the chairman can declare the price fixed.

THE GOLD STANDARD

In 1717, Sir Isaac Newton who became Master of the Royal Mint in 1698, introduced what was to later become the 'gold standard', setting a price of £4.25 per troy oz (equivalent to £137 per kg) that was to last for 200 years. The gold standard was formally adopted by Great Britain in 1816, by Germany in 1871 and by the USA in 1900. In 1933, President Roosevelt banned the export of gold, halted the convertibility of paper dollars into gold, ordered US citizens to hand in all the gold they had, and the next year established a price for gold of $35 per ounce. This lasted until 1968, when gold was allowed to float freely, on the foreign exchange markets, reaching an all-time high of nearly $900 per oz in 1980.

82 *French merchants buying shoes with gold artefacts at the Lendit Fair, near St Denis, late 14th century.*

GOLD AND GREED

The allure of gold is seemingly endless, and this fascination is reflected in the myths that have arisen around those seeking, hiding, or controlling it. Stories about the adventures of the gold-rush prospectors of the last century, and of the crimes, and even wars, that gold fever has started, are legion. No mythology can compare, however, with the reality behind the biggest gold-mining swindle ever to unravel.

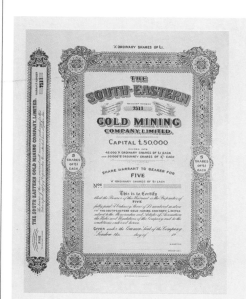

BRE-X

The story starts with a small Canadian mining company called Bre-X. In mid-1993, it had bought exploration territory in the jungle of Kalimantan, Indonesia (on the southern part of the island of Borneo) at a place called Busang.

By March 1995, after reporting encouraging results from some diamond drilling, Bre-X shares were trading at C$2 on the Alberta stock exchange. In July, after the announcement of further discoveries, the shares soared to C$14.87. In April 1996, Bre-X reported estimated levels of about 773 tonnes of gold in 267 million tonnes ore, at 2.8 g of gold per tonne of ore, and in May the shares were at a level of C$27 (after a 'ten-for-one stock split' – when for each

GOLD NEAR LONDON?

The Bre-X gold scam was certainly not the first attempt to raise money by bogus claims of gold finds. In January 1935, a claim that gold had been discovered at Charing in Kent, southeast of London, UK led to the issue of shares in The South-Eastern Gold Mining Company Limited. The claims were completely bogus and shareholders inevitably lost all their money. Simple consultation of a geological map of this region would confirm to any geologist that the chances of finding gold in southern Britain are extremely remote.

83 Bogus share certificate.

share a shareholder owns, they are issued with 10 new ones, each worth one-tenth of the original share). By early 1997, the resource estimate had grown to 2,200 tonnes of gold in 889 million tonnes of ore, at 2.48 g of gold per tonne of ore, with a potential of 6,200 tonnes, and the Bre-X stake in the venture was valued at US$ 11.2 billion.

At the peak of speculation, the potential gold reserves of Busang were thought to be likely to exceed 6,200 tonnes. This is equivalent to 13 years of gold production from all the South African mines currently in operation.

84 Members of the Bre-X geological team at the Busang prospect who were implicated in the infamous gold exploration scandal in 1997.

Latin America

Special feature
this issue   B1-B8, C1-C24

Band-Ore

More drill results
from Thorne project   Page 3

Diamonds

Messina tests
Liqhobong project   Page 6

High River

Drilling extends
gold zones at Taparko Page 14

The Northern Miner

Vol. 83 No. 6 Since 1915   **NORTH AMERICA'S MINING NEWSPAPER**   April 7, 1997 $1.75 +GST

Bre-X's credibility undermined as suspicions mount
Assay lab's results are only as good as the samples it receives

Mystery persists over de Guzman's

85 *Headlines from* The Northern Miner *in April 1997, the first newspaper to break the news of the scandal.*

86 *Bre-X geologist Michael de Guzman on the outcrop at Busang. De Guzman was later to commit suicide, by jumping from a helicopter in March 1997, shortly before it was announced that the independent sampling failed to corroborate the reported gold values.*

INVESTIGATION

Normally, before investors provide capital on the basis of future production, a process called a 'due diligence review' is carried out by a team of experts, to ensure that everything is as the company seeking the capital claims it to be. At Busang, this review was not carried out when it should have been, apparently due to oversights by investment houses and stock exchanges. Indeed, it was only in March 1997, when the US mining company Freeport was brought in as a potential partner, that the review process was carried out.

The investigators drilled parallel or 'twin' holes to those drilled by Bre-X, tested the rocks for gold and found almost nothing. Not surprisingly, Freeport then recommended an independent review, and when this also came up with nothing, the game was up. The fraud had involved the age-old trick of 'salting' – adding gold from elsewhere to the specimens of drill core sent for assay.

LOSERS

Needless to say, the shares in Bre-X became virtually worthless overnight. Inevitably, when the share price was at a high, certain of the Bre-X directors could not resist selling shares to bring in a few million dollars of cash. However, many company executives were among the greatest losers, along with small investors, and some of the mutual funds; not least was the Indonesian Suharto nepocracy, which itself was to fall early in 1998. Investment in gold exploration was seriously affected worldwide.

'Thinking to get at once all the gold the goose could give, he killed it and opened it only to find, – nothing.'

Aesop, Fables, 6th century BC

ORNAMENT AND JEWELLERY

That gold could be beaten extremely thin was known in ancient times, and both the art of beating gold and the art of gilding have long been recognized as important crafts. In about 3000 BC, early forms of gilding involved simply wrapping gold foil around silver objects. This was improved by applying an adhesive beneath the foil, and also by burnishing. In AD 77, Pliny the Elder described gilding using adhesive made from the white of an egg, and also gilding with the aid of mercury, which, although costly in the 1st century AD, was to become the standard gilding technique from the 3rd or 4th centuries AD right through to recent times.

The Romans were very skilled in the production of gold leaf and, according to Pliny the Elder, a troy ounce (31.1 g) could be beaten so thin that 750 leaves, each approximately 9 cm², could be produced. Nowadays the same weight could be beaten into a sheet of gold leaf 30 m² in area (covering about 4.5 times the area of all 750 Roman leaves) and so thin that it transmits green light, or it could be drawn into a wire 72 km long. Special tools, such as boxwood pincers, rattan cane cutters and Arctic hare's foot brushes, are used to handle gold leaf, since it adheres to most other metals.

For large decorative objects, however, gilding with gold leaf was found to be more expensive than by applying an amalgam of gold and mercury onto a bronze or copper substrate and then recovering the mercury by heating it until it vaporized. However, this method still used up substantial amounts of gold.

ELECTROLYTIC GOLD PLATING

In 1839, gold plating by electrolysis from gold cyanide solution was discovered by Dr John Wright, a chemist from Birmingham, England. An early example of the use of this method was the plating of the enormous onion domes of the Cathedral of Christ the Saviour in Moscow, the largest of which was more than 30 m in diameter. The electroplating was carried out in 1854 in the plant of Duke Maximilian von Leuchtenberg in St Petersburg to a specification of 28.44 g of gold per m², the total weight of gold used in covering the domes being just under 500 kg. In 1933, Stalin had this enormous building demolished, but another cathedral with gold-covered onion domes has now been built on the same site (fig 87).

For very large objects, special techniques have been invented so that electroplating can take place *in situ*. Such techniques were not, however, used for the recently regilded statue of Prince Albert in the Albert Memorial,

87 *The rebuilt Cathedral of Christ the Saviour, Moscow, 1997.*

88 *The regilded Albert Memorial in Kensington Gardens, London, 1999.*

52

Kensington Gardens, London, where a layer of gold three leaves thick was physically reapplied. The regilding took a total of 16,875 sheets of gold leaf (fig 88).

A VARIETY OF USES

Gold and gold compounds are used to colour glass, porcelain and enamel. A mauve colloidal suspension of gold, 'Purple of Cassius', has been used for centuries for preparing purple glass and enamel. Red to purple glazes can be prepared from the compound gold trichloride. Ruby-tinted glass, made by dissolving 1 part of gold in 50,000 parts of glass, is used in jewellery and stained glass (fig 89).

Gold thread for use in textiles was made by the ancient Egyptians several thousand years ago. Over the centuries, its manufacture was refined to produce decoration in tapestries, and for religious, ceremonial, military and royal garments of one sort or another (fig 91).

Since its first discovery, gold has been used in jewellery, and the inspired craftsmanship of goldsmiths has produced countless artefacts that radiate beauty, wealth and power. The manufacture of gold jewellery is now a mass-market business, using about 2000 tonnes of gold annually, roughly equivalent to the total production of all newly mined gold. The use of gold in jewellery therefore underpins the entire gold market.

89 *Russian ruby-glass covered gold dish from the 18th century.*

90 *Gold jewellery adorns a woman at a religious festival in Rajasthan, India.*

91 *Detail of gold thread in the embroidery of a Hungarian royal robe from 1764.*

92 *Gold necklace set with moonstones, by Gillian Packard, 1970.*

TECHNOLOGY AND MEDICINE

Gold has many uses in advanced technology, notably in the electronics industry, and as a catalyst, to speed up the rate of certain chemical reactions without itself becoming altered in the process. It is also used in thin-film technology, medicine and dentistry, colloid science, and in materials science. As with any metal or compound, its usefulness depends on its unique physical and chemical properties.

HI-TECH USES

Currently, more than 150 tonnes of gold each year is used in the electronics industry worldwide. Electronic equipment incorporating gold is used for domestic, commercial, aerospace and defence purposes. The important combination of properties here are gold's high thermal and electrical conductivity and its great resistance to corrosion.

Everyday items, such as pocket calculators, computers, washing machines, televisions and telephones, all contain gold. In the defence and aerospace industries it is employed in missile systems and in spacecraft. The lunar modules of the Apollo space program have a thin coating of gold foil as a radiation shield; it is also used to coat the visors of NASA astronauts' helmets (fig 93).

Gold has become a standard material for bonding and joining electronic components, and for high-performance, high-reliability conductor applications.

Due to its high cost, electro-deposition of thin layers is the method usually employed to get the gold where it is needed. In semi-conductor devices, gold wire with a diameter of 0.01 mm and a fineness of 999.99 is used to connect transistors and integrated circuits. The gold content of the 'electronic scrap' that is generated when electronic devices are discarded can be recovered, along with other metals, by smelting, and recycled. For instance, the Horne smelter at Noranda, in Quebec, Canada, has a skip outside it for computer 'junk', which is thrown directly into the smelter, where the gold is recovered from the melted-down components.

93 *View of the Apollo 12 lander on the moon. The US spacecraft was protected against radiation by gold foil and the astronaut's visor was made of gold-coated protective glass.*

Gold's powerful heat-reflecting property when used as an ultra-thin film in glass windows enable heat to be reduced as the gold layer bounces back sunlight in summer and retained as it prevents loss from inside a building in the winter. Just 31 g of gold can cover 300 m² of glass.

DENTISTRY

Gold has been employed in dentistry for about 2700 years, the earliest evidence being of the Etruscans' usage of gold wire to hold substitute teeth in place. Later, gold leaf was used for filling cavities (fig 94). Gold's resistance to corrosion and malleability are the important properties for dentistry, but its softness makes it susceptible to rapid wear. To overcome this, it is alloyed with copper, platinum, silver and, more recently, palladium. Dental usage worldwide accounts for about 60 tonnes of gold each year.

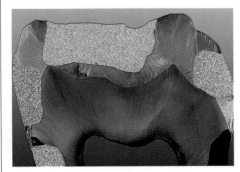

94 Section through tooth with fillings. Areas of decay are replaced with ceramic fillings (grainy) and single gold filling (lower right).

MEDICINE

Medieval writers believed that gold had healing powers. In about 1250, Bartholomaeus Anglicus, an English-born Franciscan friar who became professor of theology at Magdeburg, Germany, published his remarkable work *De proprietatibus rerum* ('Concerning the Properties of Things'). In this encyclopaedia of all the sciences, he extolled the virtues of gold for treating 'cardiacal passion', 'evils of the spleen and other evils'. His statement that 'gold comforteth lymmes' might have foretold its later medicinal use in the treatment of rheumatism and arthritis, as recommended in the book *Aurum potabile* ('Drinkable Gold') by Paracelsus (1493–1541), the Swiss physician and alchemist.

In more modern times, gold has also been used, with variable degrees of success, as a treatment for syphilis, when it was given in the form of a mixture of gold chloride and sodium chloride, and for tuberculosis. Recent research in gold chemistry has led to the development of a triethylphosphine gold complex, which is currently used to alleviate problems with joints and radioactive gold compounds used in cancer treatment.

Other supposed benefits of gold to health are not so certain. The Austrian liqueur Goldwasser contains fine flakes of gold-leaf; some people have claimed it has medicinal properties. However, nutritionists do not think that gold is one of the essential elements required by living things, and in fact gold may be the ultimate in 'bio-compatible' elements which has no direct detrimental effect on animal life.

ALLOYS AND CATALYSIS

Metallurgists have recently developed new, harder alloys of gold, such as '990' gold, which contains 1% by weight of the element titanium. This has greater resistance to wear and is used for high-strength gold foil and gold bonding wires, and in jewellery. Another interesting alloy is $Al_{11}Au_6$ ('purple plague'), which is extremely brittle but can be used as a decorative material in jewellery. Gold is used as a catalyst in the low-temperature oxidation of carbon monoxide, which is important for air purification systems and breathing apparatus.

95 Purple plague necklace made from the intermetallic compound with approximate composition $Al_{11}Au_6$.

GOLDSMITHS, HALLMARKS AND ASSAYING

Goldsmithing is an ancient and venerated profession, the working and making of gold articles being recorded throughout history. Perhaps the goldsmith's art dates back to the late Paleolithic period, when it is possible that gold nuggets found in stream beds might have been cold-hammered into thin plates for ornamental purposes.

With the development of heating metallurgy, by about 3000 BC, small gold objects could be cast. The ancient Egyptians were master goldsmiths, producing some of the most exquisite work known. In the early days of the Roman Republic little gold was used, but after the capture of the Greek empire, Roman gold mines were opened in Spain to support and develop Roman goldsmithing. The marking of gold objects to denote their quality is said to have begun in ancient Egypt. In Roman times, gold ware was stamped with the mark of the proconsul and mint master. Early medieval goldsmiths formed guilds to protect and regulate the profession.

HALLMARKING

In 1327, in London, the Goldsmiths' Company received its Royal Charter. Following on from this, from 1363 every master goldsmith was required to have his own mark placed on his work.

Later, in 1478, during the reign of King Edward IV, it was decreed that goldsmiths and silversmiths should take their wares to the Goldsmiths' Hall to be 'hallmarked' for purity. Hallmarking laws are virtually unchanged to this day. Goods must not be sold until they have been assayed and hallmarked.

Hallmarks may consist of a sponsor (manufacturer's) mark, the standard mark (indicating the content of the precious metal), the assay office mark and a date letter. There are four standards for the purity of gold: 22, 18, 14 and 9 carats.

In addition to the Goldsmiths' Hall in London, other centres, such as Birmingham (established 1824) and Sheffield (established 1903), are permitted to hallmark goldware. In Scotland, hallmarking began with the Act of 1457, allowing Edinburgh to have its own mark.

96 *Goldsmiths at work: drawing by Conrad Meyer, about 1650.*

GOLDSMITHS, HALLMARKS AND ASSAYING

There are two types of approved hallmarks: those on articles made in the UK, and those placed in the UK on articles made elsewhere. Twenty-nine other countries use hallmarks on their gold ware, but the standards set by these marks may be different.

Old methods of 'assay' for gold used a 'touch-stone', a hard black stone that acted as a kind of streak plate, but with the greater understanding of chemistry in the 17th century, the assayers' laboratory became more sophisticated.

Today, the assayer uses advanced laboratory equipment to determine the purity of gold but still applies the principle method of 'fire assay'. This is a technique of chemical analysis, which results in the production of a small bead of gold that can be weighed. Other geochemical assessments of purity are spectroscopic, using instruments to detect for the presence of gold. These methods may not be foolproof, whereas fire assay is, since gold is actually recovered by the technique.

97 *The arms of the Goldsmiths' Company of London.*

98 *British hallmarks for 18-carat gold, 1999.*

99 *The crown of St Stephen, Hungary's first king, said to have been presented to him by the Pope in 1001.*

LORE, MYTHS AND FANTASY

Previous civilizations interpreted the properties of gold in many ways: for instance, because of its colour and brightness, the Incas equated it with the sweat of the sun and they fashioned jewellery to their sun god. The ancient Egyptians related its impervious, indestructible nature to immortality so that the dead, encased in gold, should have an afterlife.

According to the Greek legend, Midas (King of Phrygia, in Asia Minor) was given the power by the god Dionysus of turning all he touched to gold. Midas was only cured by bathing in the river which washed the curse away. There is an element of truth to the story since the Sardis river in Turkey, central to his Kingdom, contains much fine alluvial gold. This was perhaps placed there when the curse was washed away. Significant alluvial gold was recovered from this river in ancient times and the Kingdom's wealth may have been partly based on this resource. To this day, we say someone has the Midas touch when they show an ability to make money. Another Greek legend was that of the golden gleece (see page 24), which is also based on the use of animal fleece in ancient times to trap alluvial gold.

Many legends have alluded to the possible sources of gold. One of the most famous is the 'Rhine gold' story, which was based on an epic 13th-century German poem, itself derived from much older Scandinavian legends.

Between 1848 and 1876, the famous German composer Richard Wagner adapted the story in his four-part opera *Der Ring des Nibelungen* (The Ring of the Nibelung). In the legend, the hidden gold of the river is guarded by the Rhine-maidens and, as long as it remains hidden, it retains its purity. However, it is stolen, causing all manner of chaos before being returned to the river. In fact, gold does exist in the waters of the Rhine. It was extracted in the 19th century, with production in the best years reaching upwards of 15 kg per annum.

EL DORADO

In the 1530s, Spanish explorers witnessed an event at Lake Guatavita in Colombia that seemed to provide evidence for the truth of the legend of El Dorado (Spanish for 'The Gilded', or in other words 'the Golden City'), which was to help fuel the conquistadores in their quest for gold. They watched Muisca Indians tossing

100 Coated with gold dust, the King of the Muisca Indians prepares to dive into Lake Guatavita, in this engraving El Dorado, *by Theodore de Bry (1528–1598).*

101 View of Lake Guatavita, Colombia, reputed site of the legend of El Dorado.

pieces of gold as votive offerings into the lake, as part of a ceremony to appeal to a golden god who, the Indians believed, inhabited the bottom of the lake.

The Spaniards assumed that the Indians had great wealth in gold and that over time, enormous quantities of the metal must have accumulated at the bottom of the lake. So began many attempts to recover these riches and other promised wealth in the region. At Guatavita in 1560 a Spanish nobleman, Antonio de Sepulveda, used a large local workforce to cut a canal in order to drain the lake. This prodigious effort recovered a mere 232 pesos and 10 g of gold!

Further attempts to recover the treasure followed, the most spectacular of which was in the 19th century, when a British group, Contractors Limited, used a steam pump to drain the lake completely. After washing away the mud at the bottom, all that they recovered were some 20 gold objects and a few emeralds. The value of these fell well short of the company's £40,000 investment. Many further efforts in this century have been equally unrewarding, and the Colombian government has now banned further recovery attempts. It is certain that the best place to hunt for Muisca ceremonial gold is in the wonderful Bogota Gold Museum. Meanwhile, the expression El Dorado, or eldorado, is used today for any place where people may find great riches or fabulous opportunity.

LORE, MYTHS AND FANTASY

102 The Alchemist, *by David Teniers (1610–1690).*

THE ALCHEMISTS

Along with the search for a chemical remedy for disease – the universal elixir – was the alchemists' pursuit of a method of transmuting 'base metal' (such as lead or copper) to gold. It had long been known that the ancient Egyptians worshipped the sun, which represented gold. In AD 296, the Roman emperor Diocletian, fearful that Egypt might again gain power from the alchemists of Alexandria, and the imitation gold and silver alloys they made, ordered all books and manuscripts that dealt with the making of gold and silver to be burned.

Alchemy had its roots in the ancient world, the word being derived from the Arabic *al* (of) *Khem* (Egypt). Alchemy was practised in parallel with attempts for a greater understanding of human biology and medicine. Considerable effort and ingenuity was made to find the 'Philosopher's Stone' – a stone or combination of substances thought by alchemists to be capable of turning base metal into gold. Alchemy had its own language and symbols for the processes and apparatus used (fig 103).

Early 'specimen' collection catalogues often used the alchemical symbols as the basis for classification. Although in its purest form alchemy was essentially chemistry, it developed a more restricted usage, becoming applied to the transmutation of base metals into the noble metals silver and gold. In many cultures, alchemy was

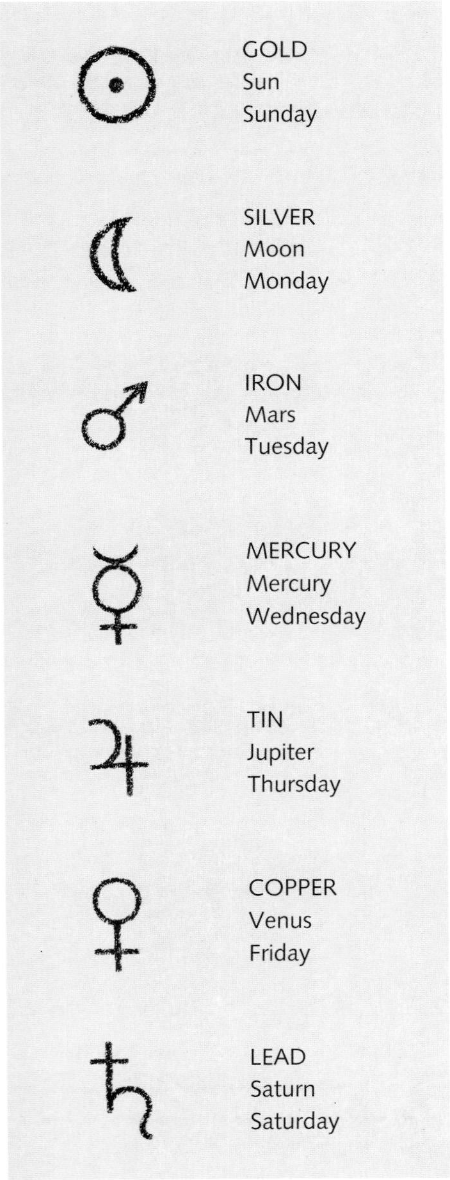
GOLD
Sun
Sunday
SILVER
Moon
Monday
IRON
Mars
Tuesday
MERCURY
Mercury
Wednesday
TIN
Jupiter
Thursday
COPPER
Venus
Friday
LEAD
Saturn
Saturday

103 Alchemical symbols.

inextricably linked with the search for eternal life. In China, the 8th-century writer Chang Yin-Chu wrote that 'if one ingests gold one will be like gold……it is a medicine which can make a man live forever……Gold is the essence of the Sun……after taking gold one can communicate with the immortals.'

'By much study and experiment the old alchemists are seeking to create not the meanest of Nature's products but the most excellent, namely gold, which is begotten of the sun, in as much as it has more resemblance to it than to anything else that is and no created thing is more enduring than gold. It is immune from destruction by fire, which has power over all the rest of created things, reducing them to ashes, glass or smoke.'

Leonardo da Vinci, *Dell 'Anatomia*, Milan, 1489 (trans E.MacCurdy)

Alchemy continued into the 18th century. Although the goal was always fantasy, the alchemists did, for instance, develop the technique of cupellation – using hot air passed over a porous surface (the cupel) to purify metals. This technique is still used in metallurgy. Although all their efforts to make gold were to no avail, the alchemists made a considerable, if largely accidental, contribution to chemistry. Ironically, physicists have now succeeded where the alchemists failed by producing gold by bombarding lighter elements with sub-atomic particles in an instrument called a particle accelerator. Only tiny amounts of gold are produced at enormous cost.

ALL THAT GLISTERS IS NOT GOLD

Because of their colour and glittering appearance the minerals pyrite (FeS_2) and chalcopyrite ($CuFeS_2$) are often mistaken for gold. Pyrite is usually a pale brassy yellow and chalcopyrite a brassy yellow (sometimes with an iridescent tarnish). In some quartz veins and rocks, such as slates and coal, crystals of pyrite are often thought to be gold and such misidentifications have led to description of pyrite as 'fools gold'. Gold is easily distinguished from these two brittle sulphides by its higher relative density and malleability (fig 104).

104 Two common minerals are often mistaken for gold by the untrained eye. Shown at the bottom is true gold with, clockwise, pyrite ('fools gold', or iron sulphide) and chalcopyrite (copper-iron sulphide).

GLOSSARY

Glossary (mostly sourced from the *Glossary of Geology*, 4th Edition, 1997, AGI, J.Jackson, editor)

Alloy A substance composed of two or more metals which are intimately mixed sharing a common chemical arrangement.

Amalgam Alloy of mercury with one or more of the common metals, especially gold and silver.

Archaean The oldest era of the Precambrian eon, extending from the earth's formation 4550 million years ago to 2500 million years ago.

Arsenopyrite Grey-white metallic mineral with the chemical composition FeAsS which constitutes the principal ore mineral of arsenic.

Assay Test of the proportions of metals of commercial interest within an ore.

Authigenic Formed or generated in place, i.e. crystallized locally at the spot at which they are found; as opposed to those components in a sedimentary rock which have been transported to the place they are now found.

Carat (US Karat) In English the word spelled carat has two meanings: one is the term for the proportion of gold in an alloy where pure gold is 24 carat, and the other is the unit weight of precious stones where the metric carat is 0.2 g. In US usage, the term for gold purity is spelled karat and the spelling carat is strictly for precious stone measurement.

Catalyst Substance that enables a chemical reaction to proceed at a usually faster rate or under different conditions (as at a lower temperature) than otherwise possible where the catalyst remains unchanged by the reaction.

Cold-hammered Type of metal working where the metal being worked is not heated prior to shaping with a striking tool such as a hammer.

Colloid Fine-grained material in suspension which can be transported as fine particles (grain size of the suspension generally less than 0.00024mm).

Conglomerate Coarse-grained fragmentary sedimentary rock where the fragments are rounded and are larger than 2 mm in diameter.

Crust The outermost shell of the earth lying above the Mohorovicic discontinuity ('Moho') which has been defined by geophysicists by its density, composition and geophysical properties.

Drill core A cylinder of rock recovered by drilling through rock with a hollow circular diamond-tipped drilling machine.

Electron microprobe mapping A map made by an instrument called an electron microprobe that fires a beam of electrons at a prepared sample. This produces X-rays which can be detected and measured to determine the different elements present in the sample.

Fault A discrete surface in the earth's crust where one rock mass has moved against another.

Fluidized bed furnace A furnace where a bed of small solid particles of the material being treated is suspended and kept in motion by an upward flow of a fluid (as a gas)

Free-milling Mineral easily separated from other minerals in the ore by simple grinding.

Fumarole A volcanic vent from which gases and vapours are emitted.

Garimpeiro (Brazilian Portuguese term) Artesinal miner, usually from the local population.

Geochemical Application of chemical analysis to geological problems.

Geophysical Application of quantitative physical analytical methods to geological problems.

Grade (mining term) The relative quantity (e.g. percentage or g/tonne) of a particular metal or mineral in an ore.

Groundwater All subsurface water in the earth's crust.

Hydrothermal Pertaining to the action of hot water.

(Hydrothermal) vent Site where hydrothermal fluid comes out on to the surface of the earth on land or under the sea.

Igneous Describing a rock or mineral crystallised from a molten or partly molten material (magma).

Intrusive Pertaining to the process of emplacement of a body of molten rock (magma) in the earth's crust.

Ligand A chemical group which is bonded to a central metal ion, making the metal soluble.

Lode Mineral deposit comprising a zone of veins, fractured rock or disseminated ore minerals in consolidated rock.

Magma Naturally occurring molten or partially molten rock material generated in the earth's crust.

Magnetometer Geophysical instrument which measures the magnetic properties of rocks.

Metamorphic Derived from pre-existing rocks by mineralogical, chemical and/or structural changes, essentially in the solid state in response to applied pressure, temperature or stress.

Mineralized Subjected to an ore-forming process, resulting in the precipitation of ore minerals.

Mossbauer spectroscopy Analytical technique which can measure some of the electronic properties of atoms to determine chemical structure of the material studied.

Native If a metal is in the native state it is present, uncombined, as the element.

Noble metal Metal of high value, normally applied to gold and silver as well as the platinum group metals.

Ore The naturally occurring material from which a mineral or minerals of economic value may be extracted at a profit.

Plate tectonics The theory of the earth's structure proposing that the crust and upper mantle is divided into a number of 'plates' that continually interact with one another. It can explain the opening and closing of oceans, formation of mountain belts; volcanic arcs and other phenomena.

Precipitate When ions in a solution chemically combine and form a solid compound that falls from the solution.

Prospector One who seeks economically valuable minerals, normally used for individuals who use mainly physical techniques such as mapping, taking samples for analysis and panning.

Quartz A common mineral formed of silicon dioxide SiO_2.

Refractory gold The opposite of free-milling.

Ribbon vein Vein where a characteristic ribbon texture is formed by interlayered dark bands (rock slivers and ore minerals) and light vein minerals, usually quartz (also sometimes known as book-textured vein).

Secondary ion mass spectrometry Analytical technique using a beam of ions which are fired at a specimen to analyse very tiny amounts of an element in the specimen.

Sedimentary Formed by the deposition of sediments which are fragments of material derived from the weathering of rocks.

Sequence A common grouping of rock units of known relative ages and associations.

Shear zone A parallel-sided body of rock that has suffered tectonic activity in the form of flattening or displacement of one side of the zone against the other or a combination of both.

Shield area The ancient (Precambrian) core of a continent that is surrounded and sometimes covered by younger sedimentary rocks.

Spectroscopic A technique that analyses the properties of a spectrum which is an array of intensity values pertaining to any physical parameter.

Spreading ridge The site at the centre of an active ocean where new crust forms as the ocean widens and new volcanic activity makes new crust.

Stamp mill An old type of ore processing plant where an array of large vertically arranged hammers or stamps were caused to drop onto a stream of ore, thereby breaking it down into smaller fragments.

Streak plate Small unglaced porcelain tile on which minerals are scraped to leave a characteristic trail of coloured fragments or 'streak'.

Subduction Process whereby at the edge of an ocean one tectonic plate is forced beneath another by plate tectonic forces.

Thin-film technology Technology using very thin layers of a substance on a supporting material.

Transmutation The transformation of one element into another.

Troy ounce A weight based on a pound of 0.373 kg divided into 12 ounces (each 31.1 grammes). Each ounce divided into 480 grains. Identical to an apothecary's ounce.

Vein Mineral-filled fault or other fracture in the rock mass or a mineral deposit of this form.

Volatile Easily vaporizable material in a magma which readily concentrates into the gaseous or vapour state.

Illustrations shown in bold

FURTHER READING AND CREDITS

READING
An illustrated history of gold. V. Buranelli. Dembner, 1981.
Gold metallogeny and exploitation. R.P. Foster. Chapman & Hall, 1993.
The extractive metallogeny of gold. J.C. Yanopoulos. Chapman & Hall, 1991.
The gold rushes. R. May. William Luscombe Publications, 1977.

WEB SITES
General
Bogota Gold Museum:
http://www.banrep.gov.co/museo/ingles/
Gold Council:
http://www.gold.org/Welcome.htm
Gold Institute:
http://www.goldinstitute.com
Mining History:
http://www.ex.ac.uk/~Rburt/MinHistNet/www.html
Smithsonian Institute:
http://www.si.edu/resource/tours/minerals.htm
The Natural History Museum, London:
http://www.nhm.ac.uk/

Gold Rushes
Klondike Gold Rush National Historical Park:
http://www.nps.gov/klgo/
Klondike: http://www.gold-rush.org/ghost-01.htm
California: http://www.pbs.org/goldrush/

Gold Prospecting
Gold Panners Association of America:
http://www.goldprospectors.org/
Gold Panning Clubs:
http://www.golden-caribou.com/goldmin/club.htm
USA: http://goldprospecting.com/
Canada: http://laronda.ba.ca/quesnel/goldsafari.htm
New Zealand: http://www.nzcentre.co.nz/hokitika/
Australia: http:// www.uq.net.au/~zzvande/index.html
UK: http://www.angus.co.uk/goldstud/

PICTURE CREDITS
Unless listed below all photographs are copyright The Natural History Museum, London (NHM)
Key: BAL = Bridgeman Art Library, PP = Panos Pictures, SPL = Science Photo Library

Front cover British Museum, London, UK
Inside front cover BAL/Bradford Art Galleries and Museums, West Yorkshire, UK

Fig 3 SPL/Rosenfeld Images Ltd
Figs 17, 18, 25, 31, 34, 43, 48, 70, and 101 Dr. Richard Herrington, NHM

Fig 8 BAL/Palazzo Pubblico, Siena, Italy
Fig 9 SPL/Andrew Syred
Fig 19 SPL/Peter Ryan/SCRIPPS
Figs 20 and 90 Caroline Jones
Figs 24 and 55 PP/Chris Stowers
Figs 27 and 28 Byron R. Berger
Fig 33 Dr. A Gize
Fig 36 Corbis/Gary Braasch
Figs 37, 41, 42, 48, 49, 56, 57 and inside back cover Rio Tinto plc
Fig 39 Corbis/Hulton-Deutsch Collection
Fig 40 Dover Books
Fig 44 BAL/Giraudon/Valley of the Nobles, Thebes, Egypt
Fig 45 Corbis/The Purcell Team
Fig 46 PP/Cedric Nunn
Fig 47 The National Trust, Archaeologists' Office, Wales
Fig 53 Billiton plc
Fig 54 Corbis
Fig 58 BAL/John Judkyn Memorial, Bath, UK
Figs 59, 60, 66 and 67 Peter Newark's American Pictures
Fig 61 BAL/National Library of Australia, Canberra, Australia
Fig 63 Peter Newark's Historical Pictures
Figs 64 and 65 Corbis/Paul Almasy
Fig 68 Corbis/Gunter Marx
Figs 69 and 87 Novosti (London)
Fig 71 Corbis/Voz Noticias
Fig 74 Courtesy of the Trustees of the V&A/Photographer: Mr. D.P.P. Naish
Fig 76 Corbis/Michael St. Maur Sheil
Fig 77 Corbis/Gianni Dagli Orti
Fig 78 BAL/British Museum, London, UK
Figs 79 and 89 BAL/The Hermitage/St Petersburg, Russia
Fig 81 SPL/Peter Thorne, Johnson Matthey
Fig 82 BAL/Bibliotheque Municipale, Castres, France
Fig 83 Dr. Chris Stanley, NHM
Figs 84 and 86 The Northern Miner, Vivian Danielson
Fig 85 The Northern Miner, Donmills, Ontario, Canada
Fig 91 BAL/Weltliche und Geistliche Schatzkammer, Vienna, Austria
Fig 92 Cobra and Bellamy, London
Fig 93 NASA
Fig 94 SPL/Volker Steger
Fig 95 The World Gold Council, London/Mintek, Johannesburg, South Africa
Figs 96, 97 and 98 The Worshipful Company of Goldsmithsi
Fig 99 BAL/Magyar Nemzeti Galeria, Budapest, Hungary
Fig 100 BAL/British Museum, London, UK
Fig 102 BAL/Rafael Valls Gallery, London, UK

Illustrations by: Ray Burrows (Fig 103), Gary Hincks (Figs 16, 21, 28, 30, 32 and 38), Sue Perks (Figs 15, 50 and 80)

SPECIMEN NUMBERS FOR IMAGES FROM THE NATURAL HISTORY MUSEUM, LONDON
Fig 2 – BM.1991,71; Fig 5 – BM.1981,458; Fig 6 – BM.27308; Fig 7 – BM.44728; Fig 73 – BM.87500; Fig 75 – BM.3558

ACKNOWLEDGEMENTS
The authors would like to thank the following staff at The Natural History Museum – Harry Taylor and Phil Hurst for their excellent photography, and the curators in the Department of Mineralogy for access to important collection material held there.

Thanks also to Barney Berger, Andy Gize, Alan Criddle and Rio Tinto for additional images. Particular acknowledgement is made to publications of the World Gold Council, Gold Bulletin and Gold Insitutute and the Precious Metals Outlook bulletins of Andrew Smith, formerly of UBS.

The authors also wish to thank Jeremy Richards (University of Alberta, USA) and Rob Ixer (University of Birmingham, UK) for critical reviews of the manuscript.

Design: Peter Dolton
Editor: Jonathan Elphick
Picture research: Emily Hedges
Colour reproduction by Atlas Mediacom Pte Ltd., Singapore
Printed by Vallardi Industrie Grafiche S.p.A., Milan, Italy

Facing page *A gold pour at the Kelian gold mine, East Kalimantan, Indonesia.*

Back cover *Gold specimen from the Eagle's Nest mine, California.*